CRC Publications
2850 Kalamazoo Avenue SE
Grand Rapids, Michigan

Text illustrations: Paul Stoub

**Library of Congress Cataloging-in-Publication Data**
Songs for LiFE.
    1 score.
    Hymns for voice and keyboard instrument, with chord symbols; some include descants and parts for Orff instruments.
    Part of the LiFE (Living in Faith Everyday) curriculum, published in cooperation with the Reformed Church in America.
    Includes index.
    ISBN 1-56212-070-0
    1. Hymns, English—Juvenile. 2. Christian Reformed Church—Hymns. 3. Reformed Church in America—Hymns. I. Christian Reformed Church. II. Reformed Church in America.
M2193.S6935   1994          94-40068
                                     CIP
                                   AC M

10 9 8 7 6 5 4 3 2 1

# Contents

## Key to Music Terms, Symbols, and Abbreviations

c.        for Latin word (*circa* = "around") meaning "around a certain date"

Capo      for guitarists, to indicate an alternative key; see chart on page 315

CM        common meter (poetry in four-line stanzas, each with the following number of syllables: 8,6,8,6)

CMD       common meter double (eight lines)

D.C.      for Italian words (*da capo* = "the head") meaning "go back to the beginning"

Fine      Italian word meaning "the end" (pronounced "FEE-nay")

LM        long meter (poetry in four-line stanzas, each with eight syllables)

LMD       long meter double (eight lines)

SM        short meter (poetry in four-line stanzas, each with the following number of syllables: 6,6,8,6)

SMD       short meter double (eight lines)

⌐ ¬       introduction marks for an accompanist

# Preface

Welcome to *Songs for LiFE*, a hymnal for children of all ages, especially those in preschool through sixth grade. Our work on this collection of worship songs began with a vision of providing a resource for the "gathering time" in church-education programs, when all the children often sing together as a group before dividing into smaller groups. Most church-education curricula provide abundant resources for those smaller group sessions, both for children and leaders, but have seldom addressed needs of children and leaders who sing and worship together.

Therefore we developed *Songs for LiFE* as part of the new LiFE curriculum (Living in Faith Everyday) published by CRC Publications in cooperation with the Reformed Church in America. A committee of six—three from the United States and three from Canada—worked for three years in developing the contents of this hymnal. Although it is part of an entire curriculum, *Songs for LiFE* is intended for use in other settings as well—families, children's choirs, day schools, private study on keyboard, and in public worship as a supplementary pew hymnal.

*Songs for LiFE* includes 252 songs carefully selected from different lands and cultures. You'll find historic hymns of the faith, new psalm settings and Scripture choruses, and simple call-and-response songs. The keyboard arrangements are usually simple, with autoharp/guitar chords included. Many songs include descants and instrumental accompaniments. To aid leaders in using the hymnal, we are also providing cassettes and a leader's edition. The leader's edition contains teaching and liturgical suggestions for each song and a complete worship-education program.

Our thanks to the staff at CRC Publications and the many who helped prepare this collection of songs to give expression to our faith and bring praise to God. May these songs help us live in faith every day, and may many of these songs become for us songs for life.

Norma deWaal Malefyt
Joanne Hamilton
Fran Huberts
Charlotte Larsen
Bert Polman
Richard L. Van Oss
Emily R. Brink, *editor*

# Meeting With God's People

# 1 A Psalm for Singing

*May be sung in canon on the repeat*

Come, let us sing un-to the Lord! Come, let us

sing un-to the Lord! And let us make a joy-ful

noise un-to the Rock of our sal-va - tion!

The Lord is a great God and a

great King o-ver all the earth. The Lord is a

Words: Psalm 95:1-3; adapted from the anthem *A Psalm for Singing*
Music: Charles Kirby II, 1975; arranged by Norma de Waal Malefyt, 1992

great God and a great King o - ver all the earth.

# Come, Let Us Gather 2

*Round*

Come, let us gath - er now to sing prais - es and thanks to God, our King. God's love is great - er than an - y - thing.

*Orff instrument patterns*

*Triangle or soprano glockenspiel* · *Alto xylophone*

*Alto glockenspiel* · *Bass xylophone*

*Words and Music:* traditional; arranged by Richard L. Van Oss, 1991
Arr. © 1994, CRC Publications

# 3 This Is the Day

1 This is the day, this is the day that the Lord has made, that the
2 This is the day, this is the day when he rose a - gain, when he
3 This is the day, this is the day when the Spir - it came, when the

Lord has made; we will re - joice, we will re - joice and be
rose a - gain; we will re - joice, we will re - joice and be
Spir - it came; we will re - joice, we will re - joice and be

glad in it, and be glad in it. This is the day that the
glad in it, and be glad in it. This is the day when he
glad in it, and be glad in it. This is the day when the

Lord has made, we will re - joice and be glad in it;
rose a - gain, we will re - joice and be glad in it;
Spir - it came, we will re - joice and be glad in it;

*Words:* stanza 1, Psalm 118:24, paraphrased by Les Garrett, 1967;
    stanzas 2-3 traditional
*Music:* Les Garrett, 1967

THIS IS THE DAY
Capo 1

this is the day, this is the day that the Lord has made.
this is the day, this is the day when he rose a - gain.
this is the day, this is the day when the Spir - it came.

*Rhythm patterns*

Triangle    Tambourine    Maracas/Sand blocks

# Come into His Presence  4

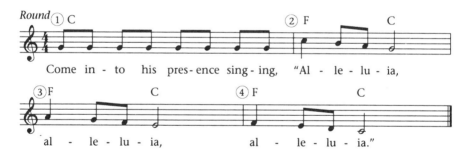

Round ① C                    ② F      C

Come in - to his pres-ence sing-ing, "Al - le - lu - ia,

③ F            C        ④ F            C

al - le - lu - ia,        al - le - lu - ia."

*Other stanzas may be added:*

Come into his presence singing,
   "Jesus is Lord." *(Easter, Ascension)*
   "Worthy the Lamb." *(Lent)*
   "Glory to God." *(Christmas)*

*Final stanza each time (especially appropriate to sing as a round):*

   Praise the Lord together singing, "Alleluia . . . ."

*Words and Music:* anonymous

# 5 In the House of Our God

**Refrain** F

In the house of our God, in the house of our God,

Bb    C    F

we give praise to the Lord in the house of our God.

F    Gm

1 I was glad___ when they said: "Let us go___ to God's
2 Je - ru - sa - lem is built as the cit - y of our
3 It is here that we find peace for our fam - i - lies and

C    F    Dm    C    *Repeat refrain*

house!" and now with joy we are stand - ing.
God; and here the peo - ple are sing - ing.
friends; and here we find true___ jus - tice.

*Descant*
**Refrain**

*Words and Music:* Christopher Walker, 1990, based on Psalm 122

Capo 5

# Come Bless the Lord 6

*Words:* Psalm 134:1-2
*Music:* traditional, arranged by Emily R. Brink, 1992
Arr. © 1994, CRC Publications

Capo 3

# 7 Allelu

1 Come and bless, come and praise,
come and praise the liv - ing God.

2 Come and seek, come and find,
come and find the liv - ing God.

3 Come and hear, come and know,
come and know the liv - ing God.

4 Al - le - lu, al - le - lu,
al - le - lu - ia, Je - sus Christ.

Al - le - lu, al - le - lu, al - le - lu - ia, Je - sus Christ.

*Seasonal verse:*

5 Come behold, come and see,
come and see the newborn babe.
Allelu, allelu, alleluia, Jesus Christ.

*Words:* Mimi Farra, 1971
*Music:* Mimi Farra, 1971; arranged by Norma de Waal Malefyt, 1992

# I Will Sing, I Will Sing  8

1 I will sing, I will sing a song un - to the Lord.
2 We will come, we will come as one be - fore the Lord.

*For piano or Orff instruments*

I will sing, I will sing a song un - to the Lord.
We will come, we will come as one be - fore the Lord.

I will sing, I will sing a song un - to the Lord.
We will come, we will come as one be - fore the Lord.

Al - le - lu - ia, glo - ry to the Lord.

3 In his name, in his name we have the victory. (3x)
 Alleluia, glory to the Lamb.

4 Allelu, alleluia, glory to the Lord. (3x)
 Alleluia, glory to the Lord.

*Fingertips on palm:*

*Words and Music:* Max Dyer

# 9 I Will Enter His Gates

I will en-ter his gates with thanks-giv-ing in my heart.

I will en-ter his courts with praise. I will

say this is the day that the Lord has made. I

will re-joice, for he has made me glad.

He has made me glad; he has made me glad. I

*Words:* from Psalm 100
*Music:* traditional, arranged by Christopher Norton

will re-joice, for he has made me glad.

He has made me glad; he has made me glad. I

will re-joice, for he has made me glad.

*Rhythm Patterns*

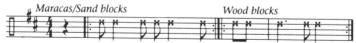

Maracas/Sand blocks        Wood blocks

# 10 All People That on Earth Do Dwell

1 All peo-ple that on earth do dwell, sing
2 Know that the Lord is God in - deed; he
3 O en - ter then his gates with joy, with -
4 Be - cause the Lord our God is good, his

to the Lord with cheer-ful voice. Serve him with joy, his
formed us all with - out our aid. We are the flock he
in his courts his praise pro - claim. Let thank - ful songs your
mer - cy is for - ev - er sure. His faith - ful - ness at

prais - es tell, come now be - fore him and re - joice!
comes to feed, the sheep who by his hand were made.
tongues em - ploy, O bless and mag - ni - fy his name.
all times stood and shall from age to age en - dure.

*Words:* Psalm 100; versified by William Kethe, 1561
*Music:* Louis Bourgeois, 1551

LM
OLD HUNDREDTH

# Praise God, from Whom All Blessings Flow 11

Praise God, from whom all blessings flow;
Praise him, all creatures here below;
Praise him above, ye heavenly host;
Praise Father, Son, and Holy Ghost.  Amen.

*Words:* Thomas Ken, 1709
*Music:* OLD HUNDREDTH, see no. 10

# Jesus, Jesus, Praise Him 12

1 Je - sus, Je - sus, praise* him in the morn - ing,
praise* him at the noon - time; Je - sus, Je - sus,
praise* him when the sun goes down.

* 2 love him   3 serve him   4 thank him   5 trust him

*Words and Music:* traditional American

# 13 Magnify the Lord

*Words:* Bert Polman, 1985; based on the Song of Mary, Luke 1:46-49
*Music:* Jacques Berthier, 1984

MAGNIFICAT

who    has    done    great    things    for    me.

④ mag - ni - fy the Lord who is my Sav - ior!

C    D⁷    G

## Magnificat 14

My soul praises the Lord;
    my heart rejoices in God my Savior,
because he has shown his concern for his humble servant girl.
From now on, all people will say that I am blessed,
    because the Powerful One has done great things for me.
    His name is holy.  *Refrain* (no. 13)

God will show his mercy forever and ever
    to those who worship and serve him.
He has done mighty deeds by his power.
He has scattered the people who are proud
    and think great things about themselves.  *Refrain*

He has brought down rulers from their thrones
    and raised up the humble.
He has filled the hungry with good things
    and sent the rich away with nothing.  *Refrain*

He has helped his servant, the people of Israel,
    remembering to show them mercy
as he promised to our ancestors,
    to Abraham and to his children forever.  *Refrain*

*Words:* The Song of Mary, Luke 1:46-55 (New Century Version)

# 15 Lord, Our Lord, Your Glorious Name

1 Lord, our Lord, your glo - rious name all your won - drous
2 Who are we that we should share in your love and

works pro - claim; in the heavens with ra - diant signs
ten - der care— raised to an ex - alt - ed height,

ev - er - more your glo - ry shines. How great your
crowned with hon - or in your sight! How great your

*Refrain*

name! Lord, our Lord, in all the earth, how great your
name!

*Words:* from Psalm 8; versified in *The Psalter*, 1912
*Music:* William F. Sherwin, 1877

77 77 4 with refrain
EVENING PRAISE

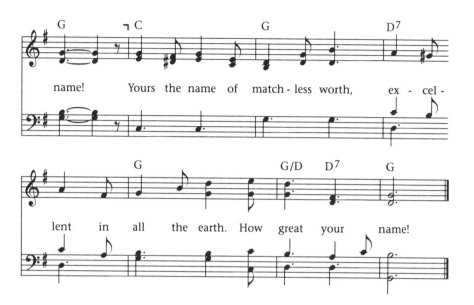

name! Yours the name of match-less worth, ex - cel -

lent in all the earth. How great your name!

## King of Kings and Lord of Lords 16

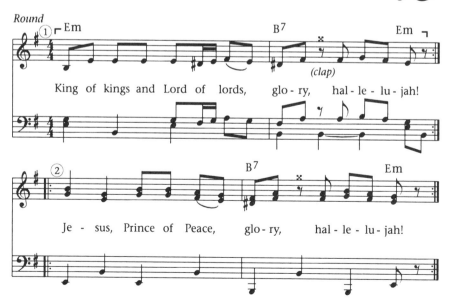

King of kings and Lord of lords, glo - ry, hal - le - lu - jah!

Je - sus, Prince of Peace, glo - ry, hal - le - lu - jah!

*Words:* Sophie Conty and Naomi Batya, 1980
*Music:* Hebrew folk song

KING OF KINGS

# 17 O Sing to the Lord
# Cantad al Señor

1 O sing to the Lord, O sing God a new song. O sing to the Lord, O sing God a new song. O sing to the Lord, O sing God a new song. O sing to our God. O sing to our God.

2 O shout to our God, who gave us the Spirit. O shout to our God, who gave us the Spirit. O shout to our God, who gave us the Spirit. O sing to our God. O sing to our God.

3 For Jesus is Lord! Amen! Alleluia! For Jesus is Lord! Amen! Alleluia! For Jesus is Lord! Amen! Alleluia! O sing to our God. O sing to our God.

*Spanish words:*

1 Cantad al Señor un cántico nuevo. (3x) ¡Cantad al Señor, cantad al Señor!

2 Es él que nos da el Espíritu Santo. (3x) ¡Cantad al Señor, cantad al Señor!

3 ¡Jesús es Señor! ¡Amen, aleluya! (3x) ¡Cantad al Señor, cantad al Señor!

*Words:* Brazilian folk song; stanza 1 based on Psalm 98:1; translated by Gerhard M. Cartford
*Music:* Brazilian folk song
English and Spanish trans. © Gerhard M. Cartford; arr. © Editora Sinodal. Used by permission.

# We Will Glorify 18

1 We will glo - ri - fy the King of kings, we will
2 God Al - might - y reigns in maj - es - ty, we will
3 He is Lord of heav - en, Lord of earth, he is
4 Hal - le - lu - jah to the King of kings, hal - le -

glo - ri - fy the Lamb; we will glo - ri - fy the
bow be - fore his throne; we will wor - ship him in
Lord of all who live; he is Lord a - bove the
lu - jah to the Lamb; hal - le - lu - jah to the

Lord of lords, who____ is the great I Am.
right - eous - ness, we will wor - ship him a - lone.
u - ni - verse, all____ praise to him we give.
Lord of lords, who____ is the great I Am.

*Words and Music:* Twila Paris; arranged by David Allen          WE WILL GLORIFY

# 19 Oh, for a Thousand Tongues to Sing

1 Oh, for a thou - sand tongues to sing my
2 He speaks, and, lis - tening to his voice, new
3 Hear him, you deaf; you voice - less ones, your

great Re - deem - er's praise, the glo - ries of my
life the dead re - ceive; the mourn - ful, bro - ken
loos - ened tongues em - ploy; you blind, be - hold your

God and King, the tri - umphs of his grace!
hearts re - joice; the hum - ble poor be - lieve.
Sa - vior come; and leap, you lame, for joy!

*Words:* Charles Wesley, 1739
*Music:* Carl G. Gläser, 1828; adapted and arranged by Lowell Mason, 1839

CM
AZMON

# Praise the Lord 20

1 Praise the___ Lord, praise the___ Lord,
2 Thanks to___ God, thanks to___ God,
3 Glo - ry to God, glo - ry to God,

for the green - ness of the trees, for the beau - ty
for the gift of friends in Christ, for the church, our
for the grace of Christ, the Son, for the love of

of the flowers, for the blue - ness of the sky,
house of faith, for the gift of won - drous love,
par - ent God, for the com - fort and the

for the great - ness of the sea. Praise the___ Lord,
for the gift of end - less grace. Thanks to___ God,
of the Spir - it, ho - ly God. Glo - ry to God,

praise the___ Lord, now and for - ev - er - more.
thanks to___ God, now and for - ev - er - more.
glo - ry to God, now and for - ev - er - more.

*Words:* Nobuaki Hanaoka, 1980
*Music:* traditional Japanese melody

SAKURA

Words © 1980, Nobuaki Hanaoka; music transcription © 1983, Abingdon Press. Used by permission.

# 21 All the Earth, Proclaim the Lord

*Refrain*

All the earth, pro-claim the Lord, sing your praise to God.

1 Serve you the Lord, heart filled with glad - ness;
2 Know that the Lord is our Cre - a - tor.
3 We are the sheep of his green pas - ture,
4 En - ter his gates, bring - ing thanks-giv - ing;

*Repeat refrain*

come in - to his pres - ence, sing - ing for joy!
Yes, he is our Fa - ther; we are his own.
for we are his peo - ple; he is our God.
O en - ter his courts while sing - ing his praise.

5  Our Lord is good,
   his love is lasting;
   his word is abiding
   now and always.  *Refrain*

6  Honor and praise
   be to the Father,
   the Son, and the Spirit,
   world without end.  *Refrain*

*Words:* Psalm 100; versified by Lucien Deiss, 1965
*Music:* Lucien Deiss, 1965

45 64 with refrain
DEISS 100
Capo 3

# We Praise You for the Earth 22

1 We praise you for the earth, for crea - tures
2 We praise you for our homes, for com - fort,
3 We praise you for our friends, who show us
4 We praise you for the church, where we can

great and small, for flowers and trees, for
food, and clothes, for those who share our
how to love each time we play and
hear your Word, for songs to sing, for

brooks and seas; thank you for the earth.
dai - ly cares; thank you for our homes.
ev - ery day; thank you for our friends.
gifts to bring; thank you for the church.

*Words and Music:* AnnaMae Meyer Bush, 1984, 1991

LIPSCOMB
Capo 3

# 23 Praise the Lord!

Words: Psalm 150:6; 67:3; 100:3
Music: Betty Ann Ramseth, 1970

# Hallelujah, Praise the Lord **24**

1 Hal - le - lu - jah, praise the Lord. Praise him with each
2 Praise him in his ho - ly place. Shout his power through
3 Praise him with the pluck - ing string, cym - bal clang and
4 Praise with in - stru - ments of wood, for the Lord is

note and word. Praise him for his might - y ways,
out - er space. Ev - ery - thing that breathes, pro - claim
trum - pet ring, tap - ping foot and clap - ing hand;
just and good. Praise with u - ni - son and chord.

who with love ex - alts our days. Hal - le - lu - jah.
praise and hon - or to God's name. Hal - le - lu - jah.
praise the Lord through all the land. Hal - le - lu - jah.
Hal - le - lu - jah, praise the Lord! Hal - le - lu - jah.

*Orff instrument patterns*

*Alto metallophone*

*Bass zylophone*

*Woodblock (st. 3-4)*

*Words:* based on Psalm 150; versified by Marie J. Post, 1974
*Music:* French, 13th century; arranged by John Ferguson, 1988
© 1974, 1988, 1994, CRC Publications

77 77 4
ORIENTIS PARTIBUS

# 25 In the Presence of Your People

1 In the pres-ence of your peo-ple I will praise your name, for a-lone you are ho-ly, en-throned on the prais-es of Is-ra-el. Let us cel-e-brate your good-ness and your stead-fast love; may your name be ex-alt-ed

CELEBRATION

*Words:* based on Psalm 22:3, 22-27; 145:7; stanza 1, Brent Chambers, 1977; stanzas 2-3, Bert Polman, 1986
*Music:* Brent Chambers, 1977

here    on    earth    and    in    heaven    a - bove.

2 All who love you sing your praises
  and proclaim your power,
  for alone you are holy,
  enthroned on the praises of Israel.
  You have not ignored our suffering
  but have heard our cry;
  may your power be exalted
  here on earth and in heaven above.

3 All who seek your rule will praise you
  and be satisfied;
  for alone you are holy,
  enthroned on the praises of Israel.
  All the peoples of the nations
  will bow down to you;
  may your rule be exalted
  here on earth and in heaven above.

*Descant*

# 26 I Will Exalt My God, My King
# Te Exaltaré Mi Dios, Mi Rey

I will ex - alt my God, my King; I will praise your
Te e - xal-ta - ré, mi Dios, mi Rey, y ben-de - ci -

name for - ev - er. I will ex - alt your
ré tu nom - bre. E - ter - na - men - te y

name for - ev - er; ev-ery day I'll praise your ho - ly name.
pa - ra siem - pre, ca - da dí - a te ben-de - ci - ré.

I will praise your name for - ev - er;
Y a - la - ba - ré tu nom - bre

*Words:* Psalm 145:1-3; versified by Casiodoro Cardenas, 1979; composite translation
*Music:* Casiodoro Cardenas, 1979; arranged by Raquel Mora Martínez, 1979

ECUADOR

# 27 Praise to the Lord, the Almighty

1 Praise to the Lord, the Al - might-y, the King of cre -
2 Praise to the Lord! O let all that is in me a -

a - tion! O my soul, praise him, for
dore him! All that has life and breath,

he is your health and sal - va - tion!
come now with prais - es be - fore him!

Come, all who hear; broth - ers and sis - ters, draw
Let the a - men sound from his peo - ple a -

Words: Joachim Neander, 1680; translated by Catherine Winkworth, 1863
Music: *Erneuerten Gesangbuch*, Stralsund, 1665; arranged by Robert Roth, 1989
Arr. © 1989, Robert Roth

14 14 4 7 8
LOBE DEN HERREN

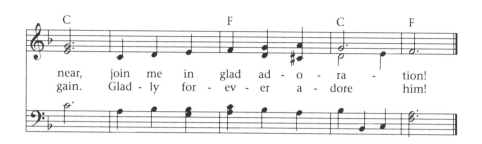

near, join me in glad ad - o - ra - tion!
gain. Glad - ly for - ev - er a - dore him!

## Father, I Adore You 28

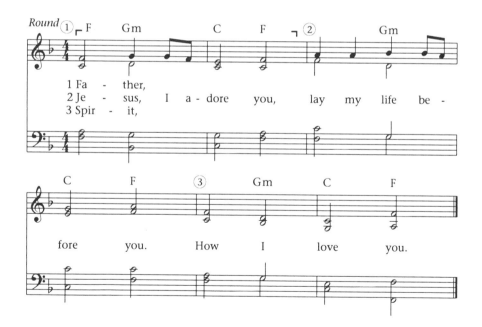

1 Fa - ther,
2 Je - sus, I a - dore you, lay my life be -
3 Spir - it,

fore you. How I love you.

*Words and Music:* Terrye Coelho, 1972

# 29 God of Great and God of Small

Piano I

1 God of great and God of small, God of one and God of all, God of weak and God of strong, God to whom all things be - long,
2 God of land and sky and sea, God of life and des - ti - ny, God of nev - er - end - ing power, yet be - side me ev - ery hour,
3 God of si - lence, God of sound, God to whom the lost are found, God of day and dark - est night, God whose love turns wrong to right,
4 God of heaven and God of earth, God of death and God of birth, God of now and days be - fore, God who reigns for - ev - er - more,

Refrain

al - le - lu - ia, al - le - lu - ia, praise be to your

*Words and Music:* Natalie Sleeth

# 30 Celebrate

Ce - le - brate! *(clap, clap)* Ce - le - brate the love of the Fath - er.

Ce - le - brate! Ce - le - brate the love of

his e - ter - nal Son. Ce - le - brate! Lift up your

voi - ces. Ce - le - brate! Make joy - ful noi - ses.

Ce - le - brate! Praise God, ev - ery - one.

*Words and Music:* Joe Pinson

# I Sing a Song to Jesus Christ 31

*Words and Music:* David Ritsema (age 9), 1989; arranged by Norma de Waal Malefyt, 1992

© 1989, David Ritsema. Used by permission.

# 32 Praise the Lord with the Sound of Trumpet

1 Praise the Lord with the sound of trum-pet, praise the Lord with the harp and lute, praise the Lord with the gen-tle-sound-ing flute.
Praise the Lord in the field and for-est, praise the Lord in the cit-y square, praise the Lord an-y-time and an-y-where.
Praise the Lord in the wind and sun-shine, praise the Lord in the

2 Praise the Lord with the crash-ing cym-bal, praise the Lord with the pipe and string, praise the Lord with the joy-ful songs you sing.
Praise the Lord on a week-day morn-ing, praise the Lord on a Sun-day noon, praise the Lord by the light of sun or moon.
Praise the Lord in the time of sor-row, praise the Lord in the

*Words and Music:* Natalie Sleeth, 1975
© 1976, Hinshaw Music, Inc. Used by permission.

PRAISE THE LORD
Capo 5

# 33 Now Thank We All Our God

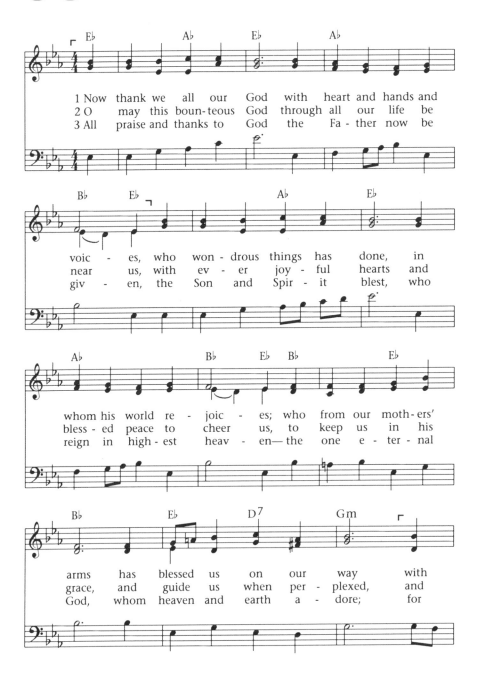

1 Now thank we all our God with heart and hands and
voic - es, who won - drous things has done, in
whom his world re - joic - es; who from our moth-ers'
arms has blessed us on our way with

2 O may this boun-teous God through all our life be
near us, with ev - er joy - ful hearts and
bless - ed peace to cheer us, to keep us in his
grace, and guide us when per - plexed, and

3 All praise and thanks to God the Fa - ther now be
giv - en, the Son and Spir - it blest, who
reign in high - est heav - en— the one e - ter - nal
God, whom heaven and earth a - dore; for

*Words:* Martin Rinkart, 1636; translated by Catherine Winkworth, 1863
*Music:* Johann Crüger, 1647

67 67 66 66
NUN DANKET
Capo 1

count-less gifts of love, and still is ours to - day.
free us from all ills of this world in the next.
thus it was, is now, and shall be ev - er - more.

## For Health and Strength **34**

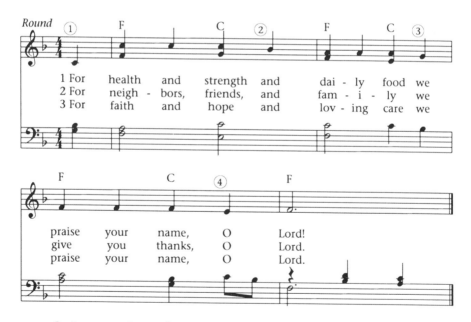

1 For health and strength and dai - ly food we
2 For neigh - bors, friends, and fam - i - ly we
3 For faith and hope and lov - ing care we

praise your name, O Lord!
give you thanks, O Lord.
praise your name, O Lord.

*Omit accompaniment when sung as a round.*

*Words:* stanza 1, traditional; stanzas 2-3, Bert Polman, 1991
*Music:* traditional
Words © 1994, CRC Publications

# 35 My God Is So Great

(hold up arms and flex muscles)
My God is so great, so strong and so migh-ty! There's

(shake head "no")
noth-ing my God can-not do! (clap, clap)

(hands form mountain peak above head) (wiggle fingers from left to right)
The moun-tains are his, the riv-ers are his,

(fingers make twinkling stars)
the stars are his hand-i-work too.

*Words and Music:* Children's folk song; arranged by Charlotte Larsen, 1992
Arr. © 1994, CRC Publications

# Jesus Is a Friend of Mine 36

2 Jesus died to set us free. Praise him. . . .
3 He gave us the victory. Praise him. . . .
4 Jesus is the King of kings. Praise him. . . .

*Words:* Paul Mazak (age 4)
*Music:* melody by Paul Mazak; arranged by Emily R. Brink, 1992

# 37 Lord, I Pray

*Canon (st. 3)*

1 Lord, I pray, if to - day some should wrong or
2 Should there be joy for me, help me thank you
3 If this day I should stray, show my heart the

trou - ble me, make me kind; bring to mind
as I should. Let me through all I do
road to take. Should I fear, please be near;

your for - give - ness makes me free.
praise you, Lord, for all things good.
hear my prayer for Je - sus' sake.

*Canon accompaniment for keyboard or Orff instruments*

Final ending

*Words:* Jean C. Keegstra-DeBoer, 1949, alt.
*Music:* Dutch melody; arranged by Grace Schwanda, 1989
Arr. © 1994, CRC Publications

67 67
KLOKJE KLINKT

# We Thank You, God 38

1 We thank you, God, for this new day. We
2 For - give us for the wrongs we do. Come,
3 Please keep us safe with - in your care, for

raise our hearts in prayer to say: May all we think and
clean our hearts and make them new. You of - fer us your
on - ly with your help we dare to do our work and

all we do be pleas - ing, Lord, this day to you.
love al - ways. In thanks we of - fer you our praise.
face our fear. We trust your prom - ise to be near.

*Words and Music:* AnnaMae Meyer Bush, 1984
© 1984, AnnaMae Meyer Bush

LM
MORNING PRAYER

# 39 I Will Put My Law

Words: based on Jeremiah 31:33
Music: June Fischer Armstrong, 1988; arranged by Richard L. Van Oss, 1992; descant by Roy Hopp, 1992
© 1992, CRC Publications

# Lord, I Want to Be a Christian 40

1 Lord, I want to be a Chris-tian in my heart, in my
2 Lord, I want to be more lov-ing in my heart, in my
3 Lord, I want to be more ho-ly in my heart, in my
4 Lord, I want to be like Je-sus in my heart, in my

heart. Lord, I want to be a Chris-tian in my heart.
heart. Lord, I want to be more lov-ing in my heart.
heart. Lord, I want to be more ho-ly in my heart.
heart. Lord, I want to be like Je-sus in my heart.

In my heart, in my heart, in my heart, in my heart,

Lord, I want to be a Chris-tian in my heart.
Lord, I want to be more lov-ing in my heart.
Lord, I want to be more ho-ly in my heart.
Lord, I want to be like Je-sus in my heart.

*Words and Music:* African-American spiritual

# 41 Psalm 51

*Refrain*

Cre - ate in me a clean heart, O God.

Have mercy on me, O God,
  according to your unfailing love;
according to your great compassion
  blot out my wrong-doing.
Wash away all my offenses
  and cleanse me from my sin. *Refrain*

Surely I was sinful at birth,
  sinful from the time my mother conceived me.
Surely you desire truth in my heart;
  you teach wisdom deep within me. *Refrain*

Create in me a pure heart, O God,
  and renew a faithful spirit within me.
Do not cast me from your presence
  or take your Holy Spirit from me.
Restore to me the joy of your salvation
  and give me a willing spirit, to sustain me. *Refrain*

O Lord, open my lips,
  and my mouth will declare your praise.
You do not delight in sacrifice, or I would bring it;
  you do not take pleasure in burnt offerings;
but the sacrifice of a broken and humble spirit,
  O God, you will not despise. *Refrain*

*Words:* Psalm 51:1-2, 5-6, 10-12, 15-17
*Music:* Carl F. Meuller, 1939

## Restore to Me the Joy **42**

*Words:* Psalm 51:12
*Music:* Susan Mulder Langeland, 1993
© 1994, CRC Publications

## Lord, Have Mercy upon Us **43**

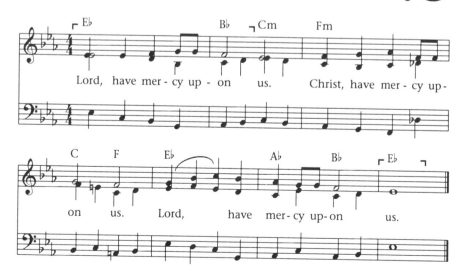

*Words:* Kyrie, from early Christian liturgies
*Music:* Healy Willan, 1928
Music © 1928, Oxford University Press.

WILLAN KYRIE
Capo 1

# 44 O Christ, the Lamb of God

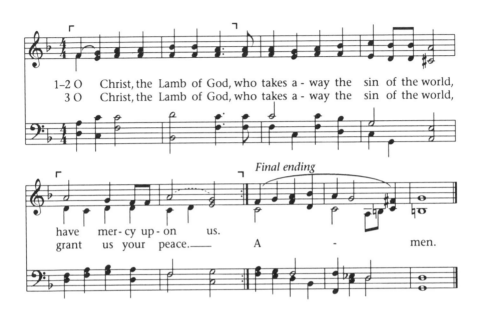

1-2 O Christ, the Lamb of God, who takes a - way the sin of the world,
3 O Christ, the Lamb of God, who takes a - way the sin of the world,

*Final ending*

have mer-cy up-on us.
grant us your peace.___ A - men.

*Words: Agnus Dei* (Latin for "Lamb of God"), based on John 1:29
*Music: Kirchenordnung*, Braunschweig, 1528; harmonized by Dale
 Grotenhuis, 1984

CHRISTE, DU LAMM GOTTES

# Give Me Peace, O Lord, I Pray 45

1 Give me peace, O Lord, I pray,
2 Give peace to the world, I pray,

in my work and in my play, and in-side my
let all fight-ing stop to-day. May we spread your

heart and mind, Lord, give me peace.
light and love. Lord, give us peace.

*Words and Music:* Estelle White

# 46 Standing in the Need of Prayer

2  Not the elder, nor the deacon, but it's me . . . .
3  Not my father, nor my mother, but it's me . . . .
4  Not the stranger, nor my neighbor, but it's me . . . .

*Words and Music:* African-American spiritual

# Praise God's Name 47

Praise to the Fa-ther, who wel-comes our prayers; praise to the Son, who in - ter-cedes for us; praise to the Spir-it, who guides our ask - ing; praise to the God who hears and an - swers! Praise God's name!

*Words and Music:* Dorothy VanAndel Frisch, 1978.

AKRON
Capo 5

# 48 The Lord's Prayer

Our Fa - ther in heaven, hal - lowed be your name,

your king-dom come, your will be done on earth as it is in

heaven. Give us to - day our dai - ly bread, and for - give us our

debts, as we al - so have for - given our debt - ors. And

lead us not in - to temp - ta - tion, but de - liv - er us from the

*Words:* Matthew 6:9-13
*Music:* Richard Langdon, 1774; arranged by Bert Polman, 1994
Arr. © 1994, CRC Publications

LANGDON
Capo 5

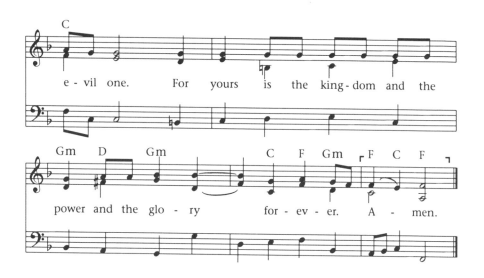

e - vil one. For yours is the king - dom and the

power and the glo - ry for - ev - er. A - men.

## We Can Pray 49

We can pray when we walk, when we kneel, when we

play. God will lis - ten, God will hear us when we pray.

*Words and Music:* Coby Veenstra, 1985

# 50 Psalm 25

Refrain

To you, O Lord, I lift my soul, to you, I lift my soul.

To you, O Lord, I lift up my soul;
   in you I trust, O my God.
Do not let me be put to shame,
   nor let my enemies triumph over me.   *Refrain*

Show me your ways, O Lord,
   teach me your paths;
guide me in your truth and teach me,
   for you are God and my Savior,
   and my hope is in you all day long.   *Refrain*

Remember, O Lord, your great mercy and love,
   for they are from of old.
Remember not the sins of my youth
   and my rebellious ways;
according to your love remember me,
   for you are good, O Lord.   *Refrain*

The Lord guides the humble in what is right
   and teaches them his way.
All the ways of the Lord are loving and faithful
   for those who keep the demands of his covenant.   *Refrain*

*Words:* from Psalm 25 (NIV)
*Music:* Marty Haugen

Capo 1

*Duet accompaniment for Psalm 25*

## Let Us Pray to the Lord 51

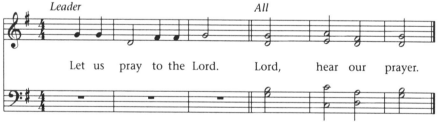

Let us pray to the Lord. Lord, hear our prayer.

*Alternate Response:* Lord, have mercy.

*Words:* traditional prayer response
*Music:* Byzantine chant

# 52 What a Friend We Have in Jesus

Canon

1 What a friend we have in Jesus, all our
2 Have we tri - als and temp - ta - tions? Is there
3 Are we weak and heav - y lad - en, cum - bered

sins and griefs to bear! What a priv - i - lege to
trou - ble an - y - where? We should nev - er be dis -
with a load of care? Pre - cious Sav - ior, still our

car - ry ev - ery - thing to God in prayer! Oh, what
cour - aged; take it to the Lord in prayer. Can we
re - fuge! Take it to the Lord in prayer. Do your

peace we of - ten for - feit, oh, what need - less
find a friend so faith - ful, who will all our
friends de - spise, for - sake you? Take it to the

*Words:* Joseph M. Scriven, 1855
*Music: The Sacred Harp*, Philadelphia, 1844; harmonized by A. Royce Eckhardt,
     1972; descant by Melinda Ramseth, 1982

87 87 D
BEACH SPRING
Capo 5

pain we bear, all be - cause we do not
sor - rows share? Je - sus knows our ev - ery
Lord in prayer! In his arms he'll take and

car - ry ev - ery - thing to God in prayer.
weak - ness; take it to the Lord in prayer.
shield you; you will find a so - lace there.

*Descant*

# 53 Kum Ba Yah

1 Kum ba yah, my Lord, kum ba yah. Kum ba
2 Some-one's sing - ing, Lord, kum ba yah. Some-one's

yah, my Lord, kum ba yah. Kum ba yah, my Lord,
sing - ing, Lord, kum ba yah. Some-one's sing - ing, Lord,

kum ba yah.
kum ba yah.  O  Lord,  kum ba yah.

3 Someone's praying, Lord . . . .
4 Someone's crying, Lord . . . .
5 Someone's hungry, Lord . . . .

6 Someone's hurting, Lord . . . .
7 Someone's dying, Lord . . . .
8 Someone's lonely, Lord . . . .

*Kum ba ya means "Come by here."*

*Words and Music:* African-American spiritual; arranged by Norma de Waal Malefyt, 1992
Arr. © 1994, CRC Publications

# Lord, Listen to Your Children Praying 54

Lord, lis-ten to your chil-dren pray-ing,

Lord, send your Spir-it in this place;

Lord, lis-ten to your chil-dren pray-ing, send us

love, send us power, send us grace!

*Words and Music:* Ken Medema, 1970

# 55 Father in Heaven

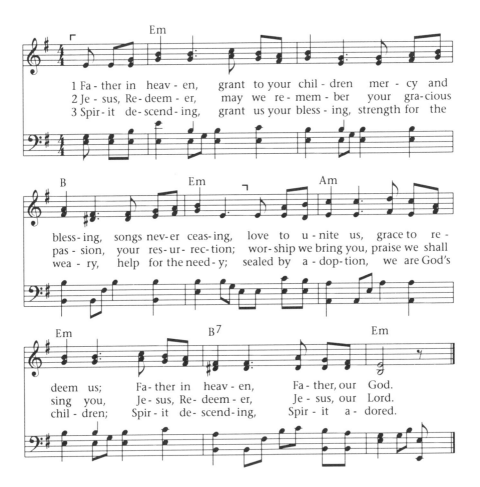

1 Fa - ther in heav - en, grant to your chil - dren mer - cy and
2 Je - sus, Re - deem - er, may we re - mem - ber your gra - cious
3 Spir - it de - scend - ing, grant us your bless - ing, strength for the

bless - ing, songs nev - er ceas - ing, love to u - nite us, grace to re -
pas - sion, your res - ur - rec - tion; wor - ship we bring you, praise we shall
wea - ry, help for the need - y; sealed by a - dop - tion, we are God's

deem us; Fa - ther in heav - en, Fa - ther, our God.
sing you, Je - sus, Re - deem - er, Je - sus, our Lord.
chil - dren; Spir - it de - scend - ing, Spir - it a - dored.

*Words:* Elena G. Maquiso, 1961; translated by Daniel Thambyrapah Niles, 1964
*Music:* Elena G. Maquiso, 1961, harmonized by Charles H. Webb, 1987

Trans. used by permission of Christian Conference of Asia; music © 1962, Silliman University Music
Foundation, Inc.; harm. © 1989, The United Methodist Publishing House.

55 55
HALAD

# Blessed Jesus, at Your Word 56

1 Bless-ed Je-sus, at your word we are gath-ered
2 Glo-rious Lord, your-self im-part; Light of Light, from

all to hear you. Let our hearts and souls be stirred
God pro-ceed-ing, o-pen lips and ears and heart;

now to seek and love and fear you. By your gos-pel
help us by your Spir-it's lead-ing. Hear the cry your

pure and ho-ly, teach us, Lord, to love you sole-ly.
church now rais-es; Lord, ac-cept our prayers and prais-es.

*Words:* Tobias Clausnitzer, 1663; translated by Catherine Winkworth, 1858
*Music:* Johann R. Ahle, 1664

78 78 88
LIEBSTER JESU

# 57 Your Word

*Words:* Psalm 119:105
*Music:* Frank Hernandez

Capo 1

# 58 When We Wonder

When we won-der, ask-ing ques-tions, teach us,
Lord, your learn-ing youth. Je - sus, help us lis - ten
close - ly to your wis - dom and your truth.

*Words:* Emily R. Brink, 1992
*Music:* melody from *The Christian Lyre*, 1830; arranged by Robert Roth, 1989

87 87 D
PLEADING SAVIOR
Capo 5

# How Great Is the Love of the Father 59

1 How great is the love of the Fa - ther, the love he has
2 The world with-out God does not know us be - cause it did
3 What we are to be in the fu - ture as yet has not

shown to us— so great that he calls us his chil - dren, and
not know Christ. Lord, help us to be pure and spot - less, for
been made known, but when Christ re - turns, we shall see him, and

chil - dren of God we are, and chil - dren of God we are!
chil - dren of God we are, for chil - dren of God we are.
then we shall be like him, and then we shall be like him.

*Words:* 1 John 3:1-3; versified by Edna W. Sikkema, 1986
*Music:* James Ward, 1985
Words © 1987, CRC Publications. Music © 1987, Music Anno Domini. Used by permission.

97 97 with repeat
ANNO DOMINI

# 60 Baptized in Water

1 Bap-tized in wa-ter, sealed by the Spir-it,
2 Bap-tized in wa-ter, sealed by the Spir-it,
3 Bap-tized in wa-ter, sealed by the Spir-it,

cleansed by the blood of Christ, our King;
dead in the tomb with Christ, our King;
marked with the sign of Christ, our King;

heirs of sal-va-tion, trust-ing his prom-ise,
one with his ris-ing, freed and for-giv-en,
born of one Fa-ther, we are his chil-dren,

faith-ful-ly now God's praise we sing.
thank-ful-ly now God's praise we sing.
joy-ful-ly now God's praise we sing.

*Words:* Michael Saward, 1981
*Music:* Gaelic melody, arranged by Norma de Waal Malefyt, 1992
Words © 1982, Hope Publishing Company. Used by permission. Arr. © 1994, CRC Publications.

558 D
BUNESSAN

*Descant*

# 61 Jesus Loves Me

1 Je - sus loves me, this I know, for the Bi - ble
2 Je - sus loves me— he who died heav - en's gate to
3 Je - sus loves me, this I know, as he loved so

tells me so. Lit - tle ones to him be - long;
o - pen wide. He will wash a - way my sin,
long a - go, tak - ing chil - dren on his knee,

they are weak, but he is strong.
let his lit - tle child come in." Yes, Je - sus
say - ing, "Let them come to me."

*Refrain*

loves me! Yes, Je - sus loves me!

*Words:* stanzas 1-2, Anna B. Warner, 1859; stanza 3, David R. McGuire, 1971;
translations: Cherokee, Robert Bushyhead, 1962; German, *Psalter und
Harfe*, 1876; Japanese phonetic transcription, Mas Kawashima, 1988;
Spanish, *Himnario Metodista*, 1968
*Music:* William B. Bradbury, 1861; harmonized by Emily R. Brink, 1993

77 77 with refrain
JESUS LOVES ME

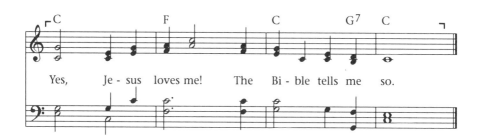

Yes, Je - sus loves me! The Bi - ble tells me so.

*Refrain in other languages*

*Cherokee*

| | |
|---|---|
| Tsis a ki ke yu | (TSEE-sah key KAY you,) |
| Tsis a ki ke yu | (TSEE-sah key KAY you,) |
| Tsis a ki ke yu | (TSEE-sah key KAY you,) |
| a khi no hih se ho. | (a KEY no hee say hoh.) |

*Japanese*

| | |
|---|---|
| Waga shu Iesu, | (wah gah shoo ee-eh soo,) |
| Waga shu Iesu, | (wah gah shoo ee-eh soo,) |
| Waga shu Iesu, | (wah gah shoo ee-eh soo,) |
| Ware wo aisu. | (wah reh woh ah-ee soo.) |

*Spanish*

| | |
|---|---|
| Cristo me ama, | (KREES-toe may AH-mah,) |
| Cristo me ama, | (KREES-toe may AH-mah,) |
| Cristo me ama, | (KREES-toe may AH-mah,) |
| La biblia dice así. | (Lah BEE-blee-yah DEE-say ah-SEE.) |

*Swahili*

| | |
|---|---|
| Yesu anipenda, | (YEH-soo ah‿nee-PEH-ndah,) |
| Yesu anipenda, | (YEH-soo ah‿nee-PEH-ndah,) |
| Yesu anipenda, | (YEH-soo ah‿nee-PEH-ndah,) |
| Biblia yasema. | (Bee-BLEE-yah ya-SEH-mah.) |

# 62 God Claims You

**Refrain**

*Dan - iel, Dan - iel, God claims you, God helps you, pro - tects you, and loves you too.*

1 We this day do all a - gree a child of God you'll al - ways be.

**2 We your fam - ily love you so, we vow to help your faith to grow.

*Repeat refrain*

*may insert child's name, or sing "Child of promise"
**may insert parents' names "Jeff and Kathy love you so, they vow. . . ."

*Words and Music:* Stanley M. Farr; harmonized by Emily R. Brink, 1994

## Lift Up Your Hearts 63

2 In Christ the world has been redeemed. . . .
3 His resurrection sets us free. . . .
4 Therefore we celebrate the feast. . . .
5 Sing alleluia to the Lord! . . .

*Words:* stanzas 1-4, early Christian liturgy; stanza 5, Linda Stassen, 1974
*Music:* Linda Stassen, 1974; harmonized by Dale Grotenhuis, 1986
St. 5 and Music © 1974, Linda Stassen

SING ALLELUIA
Capo 3

# 64 I Come with Joy to Meet My Lord

1 I come with joy to meet my Lord, for-
2 I come with Chris - tians far and near to
3 As Christ breaks bread and bids us share, each

giv - en, loved, and free; in awe and won - der
find, as all are fed, the new com - mu - ni -
proud di - vi - sion ends; the love that made us,

to re - call his life laid down for me.
ty of love in Christ's com - mu - nion bread.
makes us one, and strang - ers now are friends.

4 And thus with joy we meet our Lord;
  his presence, always near,
  is in such friendship better known:
  we see and praise him here.

5 Together met, together bound,
  we'll go our different ways;
  and as his people in the world,
  we'll live and speak his praise.

*Words:* Brian Wren, 1968, revised 1977
*Music:* American; harmonized by Annabel Morris Buchanan, 1938

CM
LAND OF REST
Capo 5

# As Your Family, Lord, Meet Us Here 65

As your family, Lord, meet us here,
 as your family, Lord, meet us here,
 as your family, Lord, meet us here,
 O Lord, meet us here.

At your table, Lord, we are fed,
 at your table, Lord, we are fed,
 at your table, Lord, we are fed,
 O Lord, feed us here.

Fill our spirits, Lord, with your love,
 fill our spirits, Lord, with your love,
 fill our spirits, Lord, with your love,
 O Lord, with your love.

Make us faithful, Lord, to your will,
 make us faithful, Lord, to your will,
 make us faithful, Lord, to your will,
 O Lord, to your will.

As your family, Lord, meet us here,
 as your family, Lord, meet us here,
 as your family, Lord, meet us here,
 O Lord, meet us here.

*Words:* Anonymous
*Music:* KUM BA YAH, see no. 53

# 66 "Holy, Holy, Holy"
### "Santo, Santo, Santo"

"Holy, ho - ly, ho - ly," an - gel hosts are sing - ing.
"San - to, san - to, san - to," can - tan se - ra - fi - nes.

"Ho - ly, ho - ly, ho - ly is the Lord our God.
"San - to, san - to, san - to, Dios es el Se - ñor.

Ho - ly, ho - ly, ho - ly is God, the Lord of might. Your
San - to, san - to, san - to es fuer - te nue - stro Dios. Tu

glo - ry fills the heav - ens, your glo - ry fills the earth." Ho -
glo - ria lle - na los cie - los, la tie - rra lle - na es - tá." Ho -

*Words:* based on Isaiah 6:3; English paraphrase by Bert Polman, 1985
*Music:* Spanish; harmonized by AnnaMae Meyer Bush, 1985
Words and harm. © 1987, CRC Publications

MERENGUE

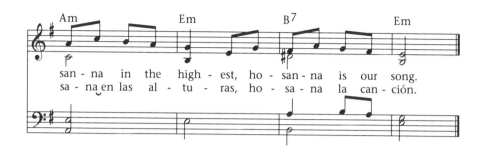

san - na in the high - est, ho - san - na is our song.
sa - na en las al - tu - ras, ho - sa - na la can - ción.

## Christ Has Died, Christ Is Risen 67

*Repeated sections are sung first by leader, then by all.*

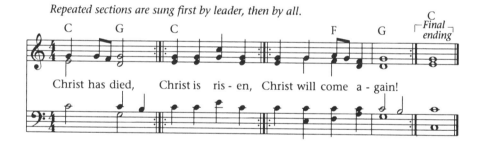

Christ has died, Christ is ris - en, Christ will come a - gain!

*Words:* from an ancient liturgy for the Lord's Supper
*Music:* James A. Kriewald
Music © 1985, The United Methodist Publishing House

# 68 Sing Alleluia

**Tambourine**

**Hand Drum**

Dm / Gm / A / Dm

1 Peo - ple, all, come sing and shout; God is in us dwell-ing.
2 Ev - ery one a child of God, sis - ter or a broth - er.
3 For the gifts that we re - ceive, come with thank-ful giv - ing.

Gm / A / Dm

Spread the joy - ful news a - bout; sing with voic - es swell - ing.
All who know the love of God, share with one an - oth - er.
Let the prom - ise we be - lieve light the life we're liv - ing.

**Refrain** D / G / A / D

Sing al - le - lu - ia, sing al - le - lu - ia;

*Words and Music:* Sue Ellen Page, 1968; revised 1986 by Eric D. Johnson

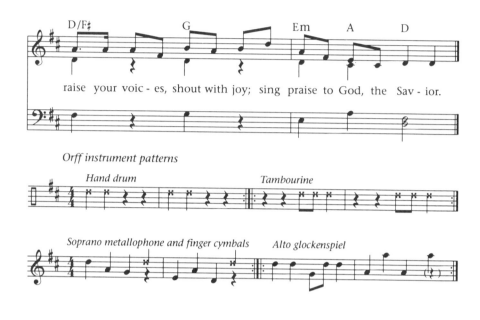

raise your voic - es, shout with joy; sing praise to God, the Sav - ior.

*Orff instrument patterns*

*Hand drum*　　　　　　　　　　*Tambourine*

*Soprano metallophone and finger cymbals*　　*Alto glockenspiel*

## All Good Gifts Around Us 69

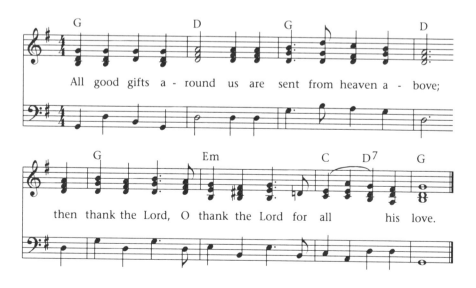

All good gifts a - round us are sent from heaven a - bove;

then thank the Lord, O thank the Lord for all his love.

*Words:* Matthias Claudius, 1782; translated by Jane Montgomery Campbell, 1861.　　WIR PFLUGEN
From the hymn "We Plow the Fields and Scatter."
*Music:* Johann A. P. Schulz, 1800; harmonized by John B. Dykes, 1861

# 70 The Wise May Bring Their Learning

1 The wise may bring their learn - ing, the
2 We too would bring our trea - sures to
3 We'll bring hearts filled with lov - ing, we'll

rich may bring their wealth, and some may bring their
of - fer to the King. We have no wealth or
bring our thank - ful praise, while al - ways hum - bly

great - ness, and some their strength and health.
learn - ing— what trea - sures shall we bring?
try - ing to fol - low in God's ways.

*Words:* adapted from *The Book of Praise for Children*, 1881
*Music:* Melchior Vulpius, 1609

76 76
CHRISTUS, DER IST MEIN LEBEN

# Lord, Be Glorified 71

*Descant*

1 In my life, Lord, I will glo - ri - fy, glo - ri - fy.

D    Bm    G    A    C    A

1 In my life, Lord, be glo - ri - fied, be glo - ri - fied.

In my life, Lord, I will glo - ri - fy you.

D    Bm    Em    A⁷    D

In my life, Lord, be glo - ri - fied to - day.

2 In my song, Lord . . . .     3 In your church, Lord . . . .

*Other stanzas may also be added: home, school, class, and so on.*

*Words and Music:* Bob Kilpatrick, 1978

BE GLORIFIED

# 72 May the Mind of Christ, My Savior

**Descant**

4 May the love of Je - sus fill me as the
5 May we run the race be - fore us, strong and

1 May the mind of Christ, my Sav - ior, live in
2 May the word of God dwell rich - ly in my
3 May the peace of God, my Fa - ther, rule my

wa - ters fill the sea. Him ex - alt - ing,
brave to face the foe, look - ing on - ly

me from day to day, by his love and
heart from hour to hour, so that all may
life in ev - ery - thing, that I may be

self a - bas - ing: this is vic - to - ry.
un - to Je - sus as we on - ward go.

power con - trol - ling all I do and say.
see I tri - umph on - ly through his power.
calm to com - fort sick and sor - row - ing.

4 May the love of Jesus fill me
   as the waters fill the sea.
   Him exalting, self abasing:
   this is victory.

5 May we run the race before us,
   strong and brave to face the foe,
   looking only unto Jesus
   as we onward go.

*Words:* Kate B. Wilkinson, 1925
*Music:* A. Cyril Barham-Gould, 1925; descant by Emily R. Brink, 1986
Music used by permission of the estate of A. C. Barham-Gould. Descant © 1987, CRC Publications.

87 85
ST. LEONARDS

# I Believe in God 73

I be-lieve in God the Fa-ther. I be-lieve in
God the Son. I be-lieve in God the Ho-ly
Spir - it. I be-lieve these three are One.

*Words:* based on the Apostles' Creed
*Music:* Cary Ratcliff, 1986
© 1986, Cary Ratcliff

87 10 7
KAREN'S CREED
Capo 3

# 74 Take My Life

1 Take my life that it may be all you
2 Take my hands and let them move at the
3 Take my voice and let me sing al - ways,
4 Take my love; my Lord, I pour at your

pur - pose, Lord, for me. Take my mo - ments
im - pulse of your love. Take my feet and
on - ly, for my King. Take my lips and
feet its trea - sure store. Take my - self, and

and my days; let them sing your end - less praise.
lead their way; nev - er let them go a - stray.
keep them true, filled with mes - sag - es from you.
I will be yours for all e - ter - ni - ty.

*Words:* Frances R. Havergal, 1874; revised for *Psalter Hymnal*, 1987
*Music:* Timothy Hoekman, 1979
Music © 1985, CRC Publications

77 77
TEBBEN

# Love the Lord 75

1 Love the Lord, love the Lord, love the Lord with
2 Love the Lord, love the Lord, love the Lord with
3 Seek the Lord, seek the Lord, seek the Lord with
4 Serve the Lord, serve the Lord, serve the Lord with

all your heart. Love the Lord and love each oth - er.
all your soul. Love the Lord with all your be - ing.
all your mind. In God's Word his truth I find.
all your strength. Heart and soul and mind and strength—

I will love the Lord with all my heart.
I will love the Lord with all my soul.
I will seek the Lord with all my mind.
I will love the Lord with all I am.

*Words and Music:* Austin C. Lovelace, 1978

# 76 Love God with All Your Soul and Strength

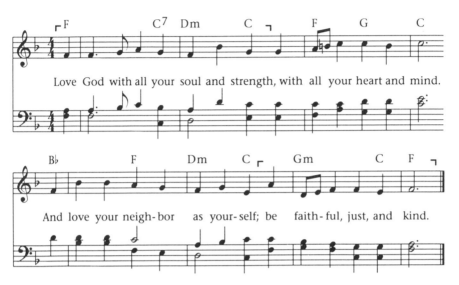

Love God with all your soul and strength, with all your heart and mind.

And love your neigh-bor as your-self; be faith-ful, just, and kind.

*Words:* Deuteronomy 6:5; Leviticus 19:18; versified by Isaac Watts, 1715
*Music:* English, 16th century; adapted by Edward Hodges, 1835;
    arranged by Emily R. Brink, 1993

CM
FARRANT
Capo 5

Arr. © 1994, CRC Publications

# 77 Father, We Love You

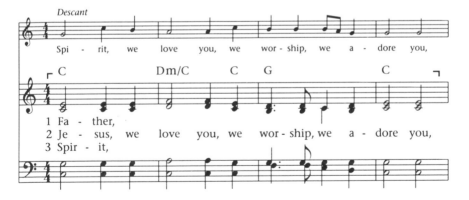

*Descant*
Spi - rit, we love you, we wor - ship, we a - dore you,

1 Fa - ther,
2 Je - sus, we love you, we wor - ship, we a - dore you,
3 Spir - it,

*Words:* Donna Adkins, 1976
*Music:* Donna Adkins, 1976; harmonized by Dale Grotenhuis, 1985;
    descant by Betty Carr Pulkingham

GLORIFY THY NAME

# 78 All Praise to You, My God, This Night

*Canon*

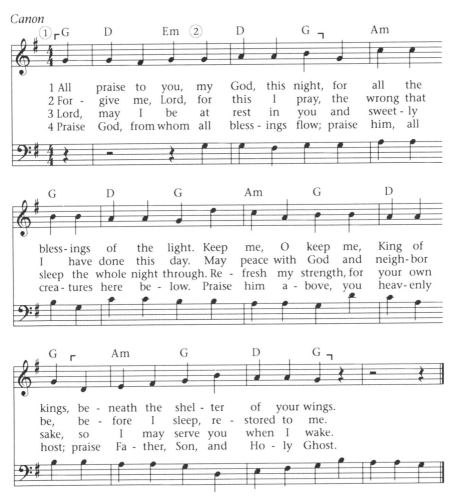

1 All praise to you, my God, this night, for all the
2 For- give me, Lord, for this I pray, the wrong that
3 Lord, may I be at rest in you and sweet- ly
4 Praise God, from whom all bless- ings flow; praise him, all

bless- ings of the light. Keep me, O keep me, King of
I have done this day. May peace with God and neigh- bor
sleep the whole night through. Re- fresh my strength, for your own
crea- tures here be - low. Praise him a - bove, you heav- enly

kings, be - neath the shel - ter of your wings.
be, be - fore I sleep, re - stored to me.
sake, so I may serve you when I wake.
host; praise Fa - ther, Son, and Ho - ly Ghost.

*Words:* Thomas Ken, 1709
*Music:* Thomas Tallis, c. 1561

LM
TALLIS CANON

# Go Now in Peace 79

**Round**

Keyboard, handbells, and/or Orff instruments

① Go now in peace,

② go now in peace; may the love of God sur-round you

③ ev - ery - where, ev - ery - where you may go.

*Orff instrument patterns*

Alto glockenspiel    Metallophone    Alto xylophone    Bass xylophone

*Words and Music:* Natalie Sleeth, 1975

# 80 May the Lord Bless You

May the Lord bless you, may the Lord keep you, may the Lord lift up his face to shine on you. May the Lord bless you, may the Lord keep you,

*Words:* Numbers 6:24-25
*Music:* Judy Hunnicutt, from the anthem "May the Lord Bless You"

Capo 5

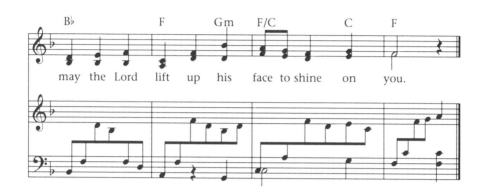

may the Lord lift up his face to shine on you.

# Lord of Our Life 81

Lord of our life, Lord of our be-ing, stay close to

us as we walk with you. Give us your peace, grant us your

bless-ing, help us to serve you, Lord, in all that we do.

*Words and Music:* Loje Braen, 1983

From *Songs of the Spirit,* © 1983 by Loje Braen. Used by permission.

9 9 9 11
DEAN

# 82 Song of Hope
# Canto de Esperanza

1 May the God of hope go with us ev - ery day,
2 God will be our Shep - herd as we go our way

1 ¡Dios de la es - pe - ran - za, da - nos go - zo y paz!
2 Dios se - rá nues - tro pas - tor en el ca - mi - no

fill - ing all our lives with love and joy and peace.
and will not for - sake us when we go a - stray.

Al mun - do en cri - sis, ha - bla tu ver - dad.
no nos a - ban - do - na - rá cuan - do nos per - di - mos.

May the God of jus - tice speed us on our way,
E - ven though the load of life is hard to bear,

Dios de la jus - ti - cia, mán - da - nos tu luz,
La_____ vi - da es un - a car - ga pe - sa - da,

bring - ing light and hope to ev - ery land and race.
we must not for - get that God is al - ways there.

luz y es - pe - ran - za en la os - cu - ri - dad.
Pe - ro Dios siem - pre nos a - yu - da - rá.

*Words:* stanza 1, traditional Spanish, translated by Alvin Schutmaat; stanza     11 11 11 11 with refrain
    2 by Tom Mitchell, translated into Spanish by Frank W. Roman.                                 ARGENTINA
*Music:* Argentine folk melody
St. 2 © 1993, Choristers' Guild

**Refrain**

Pray - ing, let us work for peace; sing - ing, share our
O - re - mos— por la paz, can - te - mos—

joy with all; work - ing for a world that's new,
de tu a - mor. Lu - che - mos por la paz,

faith - ful when we hear Christ's call.
fie - les a——— ti, Se - ñor.

# 83 Praise and Thanksgiving

*Round*

1 Praise and thanks-giv - ing let ev - ery-one bring
2 All peo - ple, join us and sing out God's praise.
3 May we go out from here shar - ing God's love.

un - to our Fa - ther for ev - ery good thing.
For all his bless - ings your hap - py songs raise.
Help us in com - ing days our faith to prove.

All to - geth - er, joy - ful - ly sing!

*Words:* stanza 1, Alsatian; translated by Edith Lowell Thomas, 1950;
    stanzas 2-3, Marie J. Post, 1974
*Music:* Alsatian round; harmonized by Dale Grotenhuis, 1985

10 10 8
LOBET UND PREISET
Capo 1

## Shalom 84

**Shalom, my friends, shalom, my friends, shalom, shalom! God's peace go with you, God's peace go with you. Shalom, shalom!**

*The original Hebrew words for this song are* Shalom, *which means "peace,"
and* chaverim *(pronounced shah-veh-reem), which refers to "good friends."
Here are the original words:*

Shalom, chaverim, shalom, chaverim, shalom, shalom!
Shalom, chaverim, shalom, chaverim, shalom, shalom!

Orff instruments
Bass xylophone    Alto metallophone    Soprano metallophone

Glockenspiel

*Words and Music:* Israeli folk song; Orff arrangement by Emily R. Brink
Orff arr. © 1994, CRC Publications

# 85 Shalom to You

Sha-lom to you now, sha-lom, my friends.

May God's full mer - cies bless you, my friends.

In all your liv - ing and through your lov - ing,

Christ be your sha - lom, Christ be your sha - lom.

*Words:* Elise S. Eslinger, 1980
*Music:* Anonymous; harmonized by Carlton R. Young, 1989
Words © 1983, The United Methodist Publishing House. Harm. © 1989, The United Methodist
Publishing House.

SOMOS DEL SENOR
Capo 2

# Singing God's Story

# 86 All Creatures of Our God and King

1 All crea-tures of our God and King, lift up your
2 Cool flow-ing wa-ter, pure and clear, make mu-sic

voice with us and sing: al-le-lu-ia, al-le-lu-ia!
for your Lord to hear; al-le-lu-ia, al-le-lu-ia!

O burn-ing sun with gold-en beam, and shin-ing
Fierce fire, so mas-ter-ful and bright, pro-vid-ing

moon with sil-ver gleam, O praise him, O praise him,
us with warmth and light, O praise him, O praise him,

*Words:* Francis of Assisi, 1225; translated by William H. Draper, 1910
*Music: Auserlesen Catholische Geistliche Kirchengesäng,* Cologne, 1623

LM with alleluias
LASST UNS ERFREUEN

## Alleluia 87

1 Al-le-lu-ia, al-le-lu-ia, al-le-lu-ia, al-le-lu-ia.
Al-le-lu-ia, al-le-lu-ia, al-le-lu-ia, al-le-lu-ia.

2 He's my Savior, alleluia . . . . (4x)
3 He is worthy, alleluia . . . . (4x)
4 I will praise him, alleluia . . . . (4x)

*Words and Music:* Jerry Sinclair, 1972

SINCLAIR

# 88 We Thank God

We thank God for giv-ing us life,* giv-ing us life, giv-ing us life. We thank God for giv-ing us life; we thank God to - day.

*Refrain*

On this day and ev - ery day, ev - ery day, ev - ery day; on this day and ev - ery day, let's thank the God of love.

*\* Additional stanzas: love, faith, hope, joy, Mom, Dad, and so on.*

*Words and Music:* Kathleen Hart Brumm, 1988

# For the Beauty of the Earth 89

1 For the beau - ty of the earth, for the glo - ry
2 For the joy of hu - man love, broth - er, sis - ter,

of the skies, for the love which from our birth
par - ent, child, friends on earth, and friends a - bove,

o - ver and a - round us lies,
for all gen - tle thoughts and mild. *Refrain* Christ, our Lord, to

you we raise this, our hymn of grate - ful praise.

*Words:* Folliott S. Pierpont, 1864
*Music:* Conrad Kocher, 1838; adapted by William H. Monk, 1861; arranged by
  Robert Roth, 1989

77 77 77
DIX

# 90 All Things Bright and Beautiful

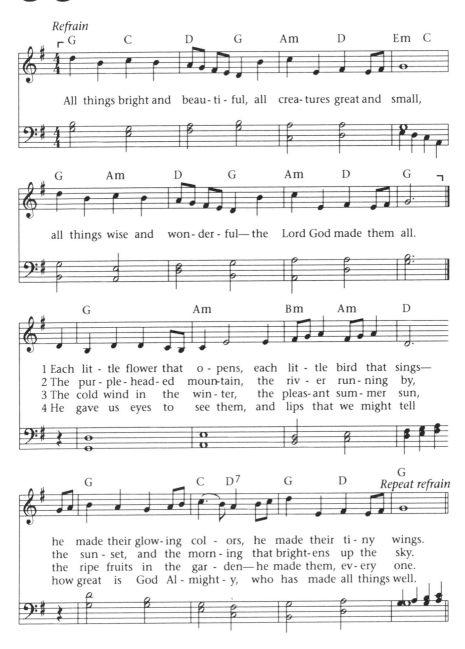

*Refrain*

All things bright and beau-ti-ful, all crea-tures great and small,

all things wise and won-der-ful—the Lord God made them all.

1 Each lit-tle flower that o-pens, each lit-tle bird that sings—
2 The pur-ple-head-ed moun-tain, the riv-er run-ning by,
3 The cold wind in the win-ter, the pleas-ant sum-mer sun,
4 He gave us eyes to see them, and lips that we might tell

*Repeat refrain*

he made their glow-ing col-ors, he made their ti-ny wings.
the sun-set, and the morn-ing that bright-ens up the sky.
the ripe fruits in the gar-den—he made them, ev-ery one.
how great is God Al-might-y, who has made all things well.

*Words:* Cecil F. Alexander, 1848
*Music: The Dancing Master*, 1686; harmonized by John Worst, 1974
Harm. © 1994, CRC Publications

76 76 with refrain
ROYAL OAK

# Who Made Ocean, Earth, and Sky? 91

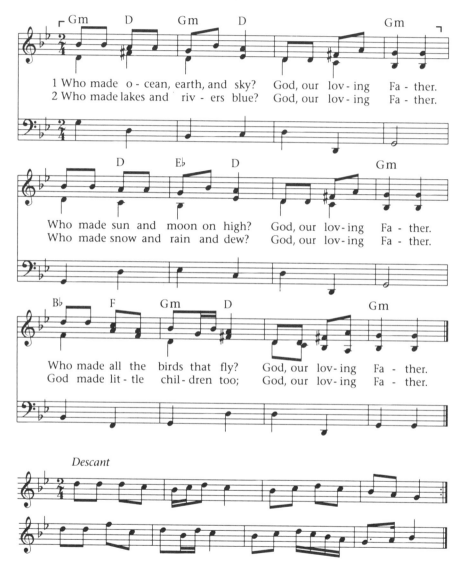

1 Who made o-cean, earth, and sky? God, our lov-ing Fa-ther.
2 Who made lakes and riv-ers blue? God, our lov-ing Fa-ther.

Who made sun and moon on high? God, our lov-ing Fa-ther.
Who made snow and rain and dew? God, our lov-ing Fa-ther.

Who made all the birds that fly? God, our lov-ing Fa-ther.
God made lit-tle chil-dren too; God, our lov-ing Fa-ther.

*Descant*

*The descant may be played by one or two instruments. When using two instruments, alternate every two measures—one playing the question, the other the answer.*

*Words:* Richard Compton, 1921
*Music:* traditional Finnish melody, arranged by Richard L. Van Oss, 1992

Capo 3

# 92 **Forest Trees**

1 For - est trees, what are these? Gifts of God to all his child - ren.
2 Clear blue skies, crys - tal streams, sing - ing birds, and fer - tile val - leys.
3 Ba - by seals, full - grown whales, o - ceans blue, and all the fish - es.
4 Na - ture parks, farm - ing land, air to breathe for all God's chil - dren.

Just on loan, not our own: we must care for them.

*Refrain*
Thank you, Fath - er, for these gifts en - trust - ed to our keep - ing.

*Words:* stanzas 1-2, Mary Lu Walker; stanzas 3-4, Bert Polman, 1992
*Music:* Melody by Mary Lu Walker; arranged by Sean Ivory, 1993

Capo 3

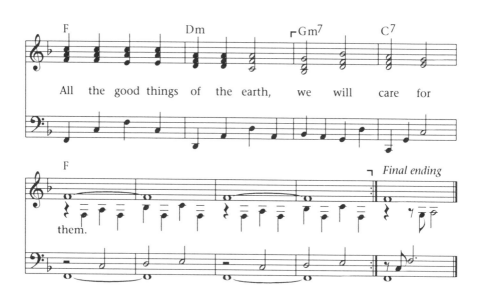

All the good things of the earth, we will care for them.

*Final ending*

## Heleluyan (Alleluia) 93

*Round*

He - le - lu - yan, he - le - lu - yan; he - le, he - le - lu - yan; he - le - lu - yan, he - le - lu - yan; he - le, he - le - lu - yan.

*Pronounced: Hay-lay-loo-yahn.*

*Hand drum*

*Words and Music:* Traditional Muscogee (Creek) Indian; transcription by Charles H. Webb

HELELUYAN
Capo 1

# 94. Many and Great

1 Man - y and great, O God, are your works, Mak - er of
2 Grant us com - mun - ion with you, our God, though you tran -

earth and sky; your hands have set the heav - ens with stars;
scend the stars. Come close to us and stay by our side:

your fin - gers spread the moun - tains and plains. You mere - ly
with you are found the true gifts that last. Bless us with

spoke and wa - ters were formed; deep seas o - bey your voice.
life which ne - ver shall end, e - ter - nal life with you.

*Optional drum pattern*

*Words:* Joseph R. Renville, c. 1846; translated by Philip Frazier, 1929
*Music:* Traditional Dakota

LACQUIPARLE

# This Is My Father's World 95

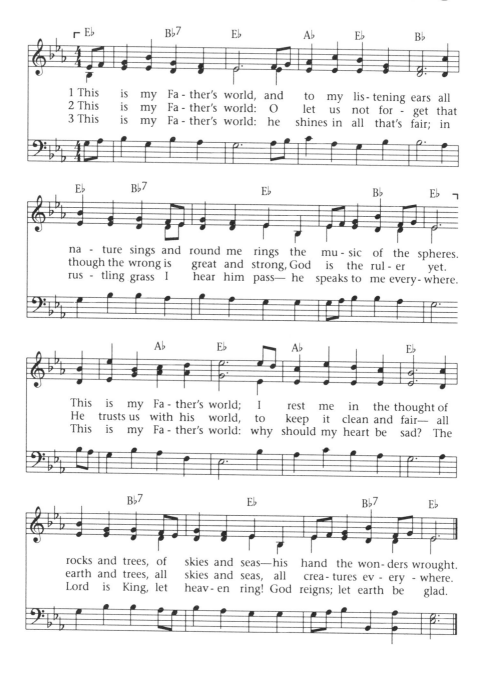

*Words:* Maltbie D. Babcock, 1901; stanza 2 revised by Mary Babcock Crawford, 1972.
*Music:* English; adapted by Franklin L. Sheppard, 1915

SMD
TERRA BEATA
Capo 1

# 96 Send Us Your Spirit

*Refrain*

Come, Lord Je - sus, send us your Spir - it, re -

new the face of the earth.

new the face of the earth.

*Sing in canon on repeat

Words: David Haas
Music: David Haas, arranged by Jeanne Cotter

# Thank You, God, for Water, Soil, and Air 97

Thank you, God, for water, soil, and air,
   large gifts supporting everything that lives.
      Forgive our spoiling and abuse of them.
         **Help us renew the face of the earth.**
        *Refrain* (no. 96)

Thank you, God, for minerals and ores—
   the basis of all building, wealth, and speed.
      Forgive our reckless plundering and waste.
         **Help us renew the face of the earth.**
        *Refrain*

Thank you, God, for priceless energy,
   stored in each atom, gathered from the sun.
      Forgive our greed and carelessness of power.
         **Help us renew the face of the earth.**
        *Refrain*

Thank you, God, for weaving nature's life
   into a seamless robe, a fragile whole.
      Forgive our haste, that tampers unawares.
         **Help us renew the face of the earth.**
        *Refrain*

Thank you, God, for making planet earth,
   a home for us and ages yet unborn.
      Help us to share, consider, save, and store.
         **Come and renew the face of the earth.**
        *Refrain*

*Words:* Brian Wren, 1973

# 98 Earth and All Stars

1 Earth and all stars! Come, rush-ing plan-ets!
2 Hail, wind, and rain! Come, blow-ing snow-storms!
3 Trum-pet and pipes! Come, clash-ing cym-bals!
4 En-gines and steel! Come, pound-ing ham-mers!

Sing to the Lord a new song!

Oh, vic-to-ry! Or-der from cha-os!
Flow-ers and trees! Soft rus-tling dry leaves!
Harp, lute, and lyre! Low hum-ming cel-los!
Lime-stone and beams! Strong build-ing work-ers!

Sing to the Lord a new song!

*Words:* Herbert Brokering, 1964
*Music:* David Johnson, 1968; arranged by Emily R. Brink, 1993

457 457 with refrain
EARTH AND ALL STARS

*Refrain*

He has done mar - vel - ous things.

I too will praise him with a new song!

5    Classrooms and labs!
     Come, boiling test tubes!
   Sing to the Lord a new song!
     Athlete and band!
     Loud cheering people!
   Sing to the Lord a new song! *Refrain*

6    Knowledge and truth!
     Come, piercing wisdom!
   Sing to the Lord a new song!
     Children of God,
     dying and rising,
   Sing to the Lord a new song! *Refrain*

# 99 Who Built the Ark?

**Refrain**

Who built the ark? No-ah! No-ah! Who built the ark? Broth-er No-ah built the ark.

1 Now old man No - ah built the ark, built it out of a hick - o - ry bark. He
2 Then in came the an - i - mals, two by two, hi - po - pot - a - mus and kan - ga - roo. Then
3 Then in came the an - i - mals, more and more, some through the win - dow and some through the door. And

*Words and Music:* traditional American; adapted by Patricia Nederveld, arranged by Emily R. Brink, 1992

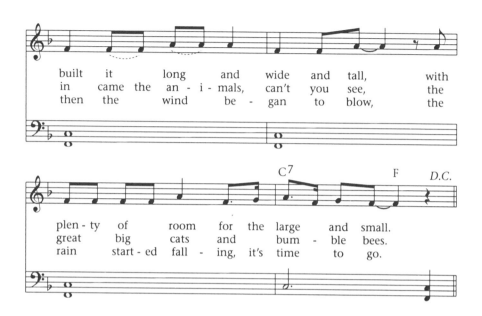

built it long and wide and tall, with
in came the an - i - mals, can't you see, the
then the wind be - gan to blow, the

C⁷        F    D.C.

plen - ty of room for the large and small.
great big cats and bum - ble bees.
rain start - ed fall - ing, it's time to go.

# 100 We Are on Our Way

1 We are on our way— to the prom - ised— land.
2 A - bra - ham went for a walk with God, who was his friend.
3 I nev - er thought it pos - si - ble, not in a thou-sand years.

We are on our way— to the prom - ised— land.
God said, "Look up at all the stars— you can-not see their end.
But God per-formed a mir - a - cle and took a - way my fears.

Our God will lead and guide— us, he will
And can you count the grains of sand on the
He took a - way my bit - ter - ness and

walk a - long be - side— us, our God will lead and
shore or in a des - ert land? So ma - ny shall your
now I laugh and sing for joy, so dance with me and

*Words:* Helen Walter, 1989; readings from Genesis 12:1-2; 15:5; 17:19; 21:1-2
*Music:* Emily R. Brink, 1992

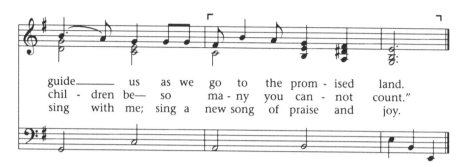

guide_____ us as we go to the prom - ised land.
chil - dren be— so ma - ny you can - not count."
sing with me; sing a new song of praise and joy.

*Reader:*

The Lord said to Abraham,
"Leave your country, your people,
    and your father's household.
Go to the land I will show you.
I will make you into a great nation,
and I will bless you." *Sing stanza 1*

The Lord took Abraham outside and said,
"Look up at the heavens and count the stars—
if indeed you can count them."
Then he said to him,
"So shall your children be." *Sing stanza 2*

The Lord said to Abraham,
"Your wife Sarah will bear you a son,
    and you will call him Isaac.
I will establish my covenant with him
    as an everlasting covenant."
The Lord did for Sarah what he had promised.
Sarah became pregnant
    and bore a son to Abraham in his old age,
at the very time God had promised him. *Sing stanza 3*

# 101 Song of Joseph

1 Young Jo - seph's fa - ther liked him best, which made his bro - thers mad. They sent him off to E - gypt - land, so lone - ly and so sad.

2 But God watched o - ver Jo - seph there, and with his power - ful hand, he caused the crops to fill the fields. Now Jo - seph ruled the land.

3 But then a fam - ine struck the earth, and all the fields were dry. All Jo - seph's bro - thers came to him, for food that they could buy.

4 God had a plan to save his own, the peo - ple that he loved. Now Jo - seph's fam - ily joined him there and praised our God a - bove.

5 God can turn e - vil in - to good, and right he makes from wrong. O praise his name for - ev - er - more and fill each day with song.

*Words:* Bonnie Bratt Meyer, 1983
*Music:* Emily R. Brink, 1994
© 1983, 1994, CRC Publications

Capo 3

## Moses 102

1 Mo - ses, go, sleep - ing on the Nile.
2 Mo - ses, go; God is call - ing you.
3 Mo - ses, go, though the jour - ney's hard;

Mo - ses, go; in a lit - tle while
Mo - ses, go; here's what you must do.
Mo - ses, go; you can trust your Lord.

hear the prin - cess com - ing. She'll take you home.
Lead____ all God's peo - ple out of that land.
See the Red Sea part - ing; walk right on through.

God is watch - ing o - ver. You're not a - lone.
Lead them home to Ca - naan, prom - ised land.
God is with his peo - ple; God is with you.

*Words:* Carol Greene
*Music:* Hungarian folk song, arranged by Charlotte Mitchell
© 1975, Concordia Publishing House. Used by permission.

# 103 When Israel Was in Egypt's Land

1 When Is - rael was in E - gypt's land,
2 The Lord told Mo - ses what to do, Let my peo - ple go,
3 As Is - rael stood by the wa - ter - side,

op - pressed so hard they could not stand,
to lead the He - brew chil - dren through, Let my peo - ple go.
at God's com - mand it did di - vide,

*Refrain*

Go down, Mo - ses, way down in E - gypt's land,

tell old Pha - raoh: Let my peo - ple go.

4 When they had reached the other shore, Let my people go,
  they let the song of triumph soar, Let my people go.   *Refrain*

5 Lord, help us all from bondage flee, Let my people go,
  and let us all in Christ be free, Let my people go.   *Refrain*

*Words and Music:* African-American spiritual; arranged by Emily R. Brink, 1993   GO DOWN, MOSES
Arr. © 1994, CRC Publications

# Dare to Be a Daniel! 104

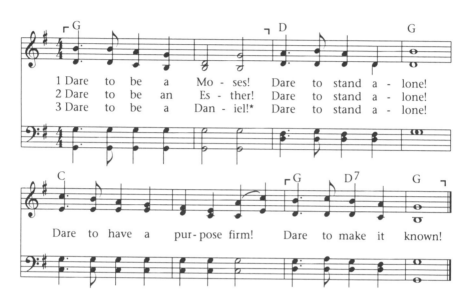

1 Dare to be a Mo - ses! Dare to stand a - lone!
2 Dare to be an Es - ther! Dare to stand a - lone!
3 Dare to be a Dan - iel!* Dare to stand a - lone!

Dare to have a pur - pose firm! Dare to make it known!

\* *Additional Bible names:*
   Noah, Joseph, Rahab, Hannah, David, Mary, Peter, Stephen

*Words:* stanzas 1-2, traditional; stanza 3, Philip P. Bliss, 1873
*Music:* Philip P. Bliss, 1873

# 105 I Will Sing unto the Lord

*Words:* from the Song of Moses and Miriam, Exodus 15:1-2
*Music:* Israeli folk song; harmonized by Emily R. Brink, 1992
Harm. © 1994, CRC Publications

PM
TZENA

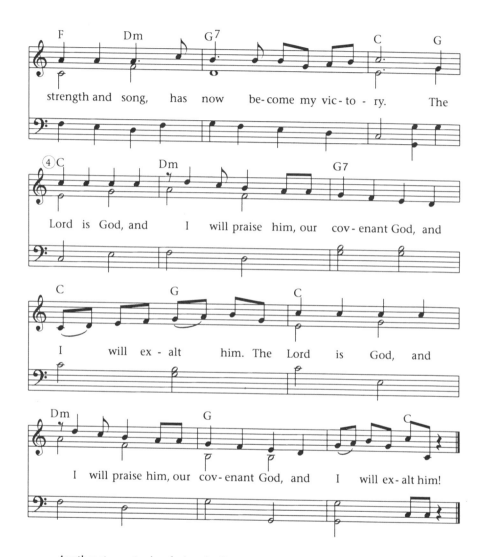

*Another stanza to sing during the Easter season:*

I will sing unto the Lord,
for he has triumphed gloriously:
the grave is empty. Won't you come and see? *Repeat*

The Lord, my God, my strength and song,
has now become my victory. *Repeat*

The Lord is God, and I will praise him,
our covenant God, and I will exalt him. *Repeat*

# 106 Joshua Fought the Battle of Jericho

Refrain

Joshua fought the battle of Jericho, Jericho, Jericho, Joshua fought the battle of Jericho, and the walls came tumbling down.

1 You may talk about the men of Gideon, you may talk about the men of Saul, there's none like good old

*Words and Music:* African-American spiritual; arranged by Emily R. Brink, 1992

Capo 5

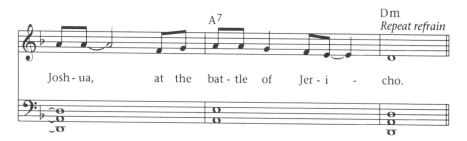

Josh - ua,      at the   bat - tle   of    Jer - i - cho.

2 Up to the walls of Jericho
  he marched with sword in hand.
  "Go blow those ram's horns," Joshua cried,
  "for the battle is in God's hands."

3 Then the horns began to bellow,
  the trumpets began to sound,
  and Joshua commanded the children to shout,
  and the walls came tumbling down.

# 107 ¡Canta, Débora, Canta!

¡Can - ta, Dé-bo-ra, can-ta! ¡Can - ta, Dé-bo-ra, can-ta!

1 Moth - er in Is - ra - el, lead - er of her ar - mies,
2 We lift up our voic - es, ev - ery - one to - geth - er,
1 Ma - dre de Is - ra - el, lí - der de e - jér - ci - tos,
2 To - dos los que can - tan, al - cen hoy sus vo - ces,

sing a hymn of vic - tory to our God.
sing - ing the tri - umphs of our God.
can - ta un him - no a tu Se - ñor.
can - ten un him - no de lo - or.

*Refrain*

For our God is good! God is good and has
Por - que bue - no es Dios, bue - no es Dios, él es -

*"Canta" is the Spanish word for "sing."*

*Words and Music:* Luiza Cruz, 1973; English translation by Gertrude C. Suppe, 1987; Spanish translation by Raquel Gutiérrez-Achon, 1987; based on Judges 5.

DEBORA

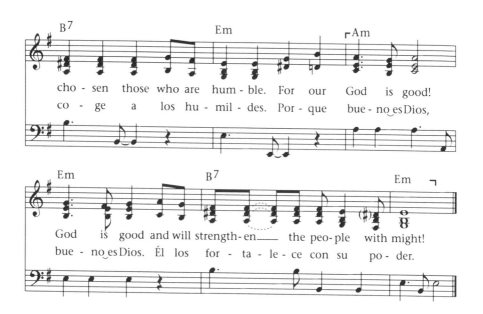

B7      Em      Am

cho - sen those who are hum - ble. For our God is good!
co - ge a los hu - mil - des. Por - que bue - no es Dios,

Em      B7      Em

God is good and will strength-en___ the peo-ple with might!
bue - no es Dios. Él los for - ta - le - ce con su po - der.

Castanets

Descant for refrain

# 108 Samuel

Samuel, Samuel, God is a
Here am I. Here am I, for you were a
1 I called you not. I called you not. Go and lie
He lay right down. He lay right down on his

call-in' to you, Sam-u-el. Sam-u-el,
call-in' to me, Father E-li. Here am I.
down up-on your cot. I called you not.
cot up-on the ground. He lay right down.

Sam-u-el, God is a call-in' to you,
Here am I, for you were a call-in' to me,
I called you not. Go and lie down up-
He lay right down on his cot up-

Sam - u, Sam-u - el.
Fa - ther E - li.
on, up-on your cot.
on, up-on the ground.

*Words and Music:* Betty Carr Pulkingham

Capo 1

2 Samuel, Samuel, God is a callin' to you, Samuel. *(repeat)*
 Here am I. Here am I, for you were a callin' to me, Father Eli. *(repeat)*
 I called you not, I called you not. Go and lie down upon your cot. *(repeat)*
 He lay right down. He lay right down on his cot upon the ground. *(repeat)*

3 Samuel, Samuel, God is a callin' to you, Samuel. *(repeat)*
 Here am I, here am I, for you were a callin' to me, Father Eli. *(repeat)*
 Go lie down and it shall be, if the Lord is really calling thee,
 say to him, "Lord, speak to me, for thy servant heareth, heareth thee."
 He lay right down, he lay right down on his cot upon the ground. *(repeat)*

4 Samuel, Samuel, God is still a callin' to you, Samuel. *(repeat)*
 Lord, speak to me, speak to me, for thy servant heareth thee. *(repeat)*
 Come to me, come to me. Children, children, will you come to me? *(repeat)*
 Come to me, come to me. God is a callin' to his children. Come to me. *(repeat)*

# 109 Only a Boy Named David

*(a)*
On - ly a boy named Da - vid, *(b)* on - ly a lit - tle sling,

*(a)*
on - ly a boy named Da - vid, *(c)* but he could pray and sing.

*(a)*
On - ly a boy named Da - vid, *(d)* on - ly a rip - pling brook,

*(a)*
on - ly a boy named Da - vid, *(e)* but five lit - tle stones he took. And

*(f)*
one lit - tle stone went in the sling, and *(b)* the sling went round and

*Words and Music:* Arthur Arnott, 1931; based on 1 Samuel 17:49  Capo 1

*Motions:*

(a) *Hand held out, palm down, as if measuring.*  (e) *Hold up five fingers.*
(b) *Circle hand above head.*  (f) *Hold up one finger.*
(c) *Hands folded.*  (g) *Shoot arm forward.*
(d) *Wiggle fingers, moving arm left to right.*  (h) *Fall down or clap.*

# 110 Elijah

1 E-li-jah planned to in-ter-fere
2 E-li-jah to a wi-dow said,
3 E-li-jah prayed to save from death

with A-hab's i-dols and ca-reer. "No dew, no rain!"
"Give me some wa-ter and some bread. Your flour, your oil,
the wi-dow's son, who lost his breath. "He lives, he lives!"

the pro-phet said, as drought u-pon the land was spread.
will not run out un-til the rain will end the drought."
the pro-phet said, as sad-ness turned to joy in-stead.

**Elijah at Mount Carmel**

4   Elijah bravely set a test
    to see which god would be the best:
    "Who will it be that sends the fire?
    Which god can answer your desire?"

5   Elijah dared to make some fun
    when all the dancing had begun:
    "Your god is gone, or thinking deep.
    Shout loudly, for he is asleep!"

*Words:* Bert Polman, 1994; based on 1 Kings 17-18, 2 Kings 2
*Music:* S. C. Molefe
Words © 1994, CRC Publications

LM
ASITHI AMEN

6   Elijah took his sacrifice
    and poured the water on it thrice.
    He prayed, "Give us a sign to tell
    that you are Lord of Israel!"

7   Elijah saw the fire descend
    and heard the people's shout ascend.
    He said to them, "If God is Lord,
    seize all who disobey his word!"

## Elijah at Mount Horeb

8   Elijah ran to save his life
    from Jezebel, King Ahab's wife,
    and prayed to God with sigh and moan,
    "I've had enough! I'm all alone!"

9   Elijah hid himself in fear
    as storm and quake and fire appeared.
    But when the wind as whisper blew,
    God spoke: "I have more work for you."

10   Elijah followed God's command
    to find new leaders for the land.
    "Elisha, come," the prophet spoke,
    "You must succeed me; here's my cloak."

## Elijah's Ascension

11   Elijah traveled through the land
    and crossed the Jordan on dry sand.
    Then he went up to heaven's height
    in whirling wind, with fire alight.

12   Elisha knew God heard his prayer,
    that he would be Elijah's heir,
    when he could see his master rise
    on fiery chariot to the skies.

13   Elijah's deeds to us proclaim
    the fitting meaning of his name:
    "The Lord's my God! The Lord's my God!"
    Tell of God's glory all abroad.

# 111 Jonah's Song

1 In my trou - ble, in my trou - ble I cried out to the
2 I was sink - ing, I was sink - ing in dark - ness to the
3 Those who wor - ship worth - less i - dols will nev - er know the

Lord, my God, and,
o - cean floor, and, Lord, you heard me,
grace of God, but,

yes, you heard me, from the depths you heard my

cry.
Though the wa - ter swirled a - round me,
When my prayer came to your tem - ple,
With a song of high thanks - giv - ing

*Words:* Edith Bajema, 1993
*Music:* Vicki Williams, 1994
© 1994, CRC Publications

though the deep waves thun-dered o'er me,
you stretched out your might-y hand.___ Lord, you saved me,
I will sac - ri - fice to God.___

yes, you saved me. You would not let your ser - vant die.

# 112 Peter and James and John

(rocking action, arms cradled)

1 Pe-ter and James and John in a sail-boat,

(rocking action)

Pe-ter and James and John in a sail-boat,

(rocking action)

Pe-ter and James and John in a sail-boat,

out on the beau-ti-ful sea.

*(casting out, pulling in)*      *(hands upturned)*
2   They fished all night, but they caught nothing, (3x) . . .

*(arms swinging)*
3   Along came Jesus walkin' on the seashore, (3x) . . .

*(two-armed, overhand throw)*
4   He said, "Throw your nets over on the other side, (3x) . . .

*(spread arms high and wide)*
5   The nets were filled with great big fishes, (3x) . . .

*Words and Music:* traditional, based on John 21:1-8; arranged by Mimi Farra, 1979

## Jesus Called the Twelve Disciples 113

Je - sus called the twelve dis - ci - ples: Pe - ter and An - drew,
James and John. He called Phil - ip and Bar - tho - lo - mew; six so
far, we're half - way done! Thom - as, Mat - thew, James, and
Thad - daeus, Si - mon, Ju - das; fi - nal - ly, we have twelve. But
our King Je - sus al - so is call - ing you and me.

*Words and Music:* Frank DeVries, 1982
© 1982, CRC Publications

87 87 D
JESUS CALLS

# 114 Jesus Called to Peter

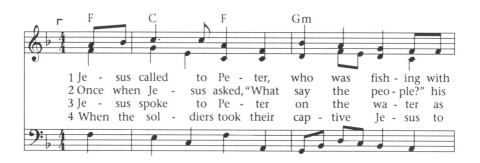

1 Je - sus called to Pe - ter, who was fish - ing with
2 Once when Je - sus asked, "What say the peo - ple?" his
3 Je - sus spoke to Pe - ter on the wa - ter as
4 When the sol - diers took their cap - tive Je - sus to

nets deep in the sea. "Come, for I will make you
friends said what they heard. But then Pet - er made his
he was sink - ing down, "You of lit - tle faith, why
where his trial be - gan, Pe - ter swore an oath and

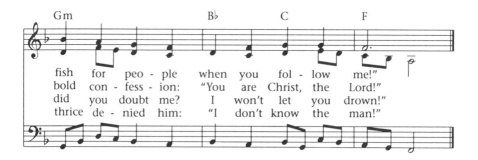

fish for peo - ple when you fol - low me!"
bold con - fess - ion: "You are Christ, the Lord!"
did you doubt me? I won't let you drown!"
thrice de - nied him: "I don't know the man!"

*Words:* Bert Polman, 1994
*Music:* Melody by Wim ter Burg, 1971; harmony by Henry Hageman, 1994;
    descant by Emily R. Brink, 1994

10 6 10 5
OF ALL THE PEOPLE
Capo 5

5   After Jesus asked, "You love me, Peter?"
       He said, "You know I do."
    "Then go feed my sheep," responded Jesus,
       "Follow me anew."

6   Gifted by the Holy Spirit, Peter
       proclaimed aloud the word:
    "Jesus, who was crucified, has risen;
       he is Christ, the Lord!"

7   Peter's vision held all kinds of creatures
       and some he would not eat;
    but the Lord taught Peter, "All the nations
       make my church complete!"

8   Thank you, Lord, for using Peter's story
       to guide us in our search
    for the ways in which we may experience
       how you build your church.

*Descant*

# 115 Zaccheus

*Words:* stanza 1, traditional; stanza 2, Herman Proper, 1980
*Music:* traditional; arranged by N. R. Schaper
St. 2 © 1994, CRC Publications

Capo 1

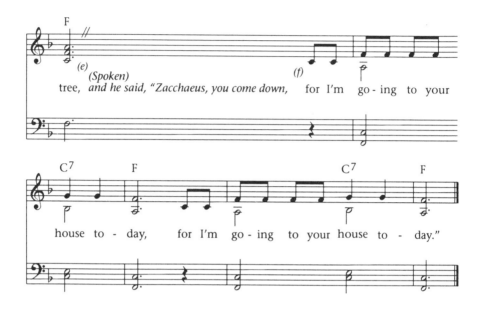

*(e)*
*(Spoken)*
tree, *and he said, "Zacchaeus, you come down,* for I'm go - ing to your

house to - day, for I'm go - ing to your house to - day."

2 Zacchaeus knew that he'd done wrong,
   and sorry for his sins was he.
   "Lord, to the poor I'll give one half
   of all my goods," said he.
   "And if I've cheated anyone,
   four times will I repay."
        *And Jesus said,*
        *"Salvation has come to you!*
   I have come to seek and save.
   I have come to seek and save."

*Motions for stanza 1*
   *(a) Hands in front, right palm raised above left palm.*
   *(b) Alternate hands in climbing motion.*
   *(c) Shade eyes with right hand and look down.*
   *(d) Shade eyes with right hand and look up.*
   *(e) Speak these words while looking up and beckoning with hand.*
   *(f) Clap hands on accented beat.*

# 116 Silver and Gold Have I None

1 Pe - ter and John went to (a)pray; they met a lame
2 "Sil - ver and gold have I (c)none, but what I have

man on the way. He asked for alms and
I (d)give to you. In the name of (e)Je - sus

(b)held out his palms, and this is what Pe - ter did
Christ_____ of Naz - a - reth, (f)rise up and

say:
walk!"
3 He went walk - ing and jump - ing and (g) (h)

*Words and Music:* anonymous, based on Acts 3:1-8; arranged by Betty Pulkingham, 1974

*Actions:*

(a) *fold hands, as in prayer*
(b) *hold out palms*
(c) *hold out empty hands, shake head*
(d) *extend hand*
(e) *point upward*
(f) *sweep hands upward*
(g) *march (in place)*
(h) *jump up*
(i) *raise arms*

# 117 O Mary, Don't You Weep

Ma - ry stood out - side the tomb where Je - sus lay. She
saw two an - gels sit - ting there and heard them say,
"Wo - man, why are you cry - ing?" O Ma - ry, don't you
weep. O Ma - ry, don't you weep; don't you mourn.

*Words and Music:* African-American spiritual; adapted by June Fischer Armstrong, 1991   Capo 3

O Mary, don't you weep; don't you mourn.

He's not dead. He has ris - en. O Ma - ry, don't you weep.

# 118 Paul, Preacher of the Word

1 Da - mas - cus bound, Saul meant to prey
2 At An - ti - och, the Christ - ians prayed
3 When Paul and Si - las sang in jail,
4 En route to Rome, on Paul's last trip;

on an - y fol - lowers of the Way.
and sought the Ho - ly Spir - it's aid.
an earth - quake caused their chains to fail.
a storm wrecked hav - oc on the ship.

In stunned sur - prise he heard the Lord:
"Call Paul and Barn - a - bas," they heard.
Then from his su - i - cide de - terred,
Then Paul spoke up: "I serve the Lord;

"I've cho - sen you to preach my word!"
"Set them a - part to speak God's word."
the jail - er heard their sav - ing word.
he'll save us by his might - y word!"

*Words:* Bert Polman, 1994
*Music:* Henri F. Hemy, 1864; arranged by Bert Polman, 1994

88 88 88

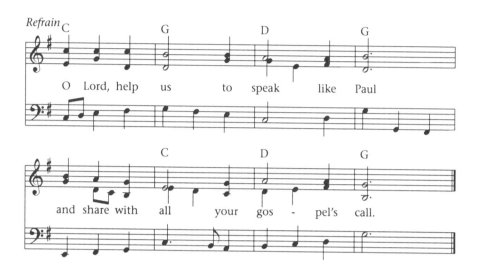

O Lord, help us to speak like Paul
and share with all your gos - pel's call.

# 119 People in Darkness Are Looking for Light

1 Peo-ple in dark-ness are look-ing for light. Come, come,
2 Peo-ple with sick-ness are pray-ing for health. Come, come,
3 Peo-ple in trou-ble would like to be free. Come, come,

come, Je-sus Christ. Peo-ple with blind-ness are long-ing for sight.
come, Je-sus Christ. Peo-ple in pov-er-ty want to have wealth.
come, Je-sus Christ. Peo-ple with ar-gu-ments want to a - gree.

Come, Lord Je-sus Christ. These days of ad-ven-ture when
Come, Lord Je-sus Christ. These days of ad-ven-ture when
Come, Lord Je-sus Christ. These days of ad-ven-ture when

all peo-ple wait are days for the ad-vent of love.
all peo-ple wait are days for the ad-vent of hope.
all peo-ple wait are days for the ad-vent of peace.

*Notice the "play on words" in this song: Days of advent are days of adventure.*

*Words and Music:* Dosia Carlson, 1983

Capo 2

# Psalm 72 120

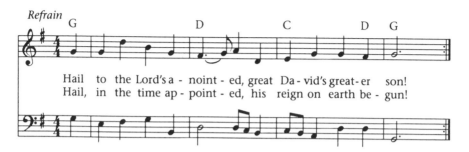

Hail to the Lord's a - noint - ed, great Da - vid's great - er son!
Hail, in the time ap - point - ed, his reign on earth be - gun!

Endow the king with your justice, O God,
  the royal son with your righteousness.
He will judge your people in righteousness,
  your afflicted ones with justice.
He will save the children of the needy;
  he will crush the oppressor.  *Refrain*

He will rule from sea to sea
  and from the River to the ends of the earth.
The kings of Tarshish and of distant shores
  will bring tribute to him;
  the kings of Sheba and Seba will present him gifts.
All kings will bow down to him
  and all nations will serve him.  *Refrain*

For he will deliver the needy who cry out,
  the afflicted who have no one to help.
He will take pity on the weak and the needy
  and save the needy from death.
He will rescue them from oppression and violence,
  for precious is their blood in his sight.  *Refrain*

May his name endure forever;
  may it continue as long as the sun.
All nations will be blessed through him,
  and they will call him blessed.  *Refrain*

*Orff instruments*
*Bass xylophone*          *Glockenspiel*

*Words:* from Psalm 72 (NIV); refrain by James Montgomery, 1822
*Music:* German

# 121 Comfort, Comfort Now My People

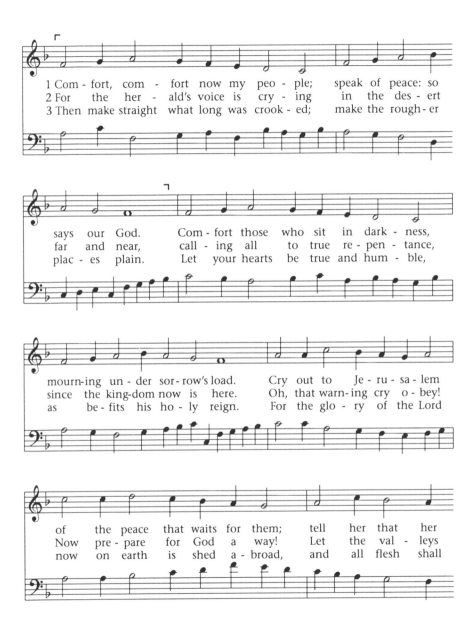

1 Com - fort, com - fort now my peo - ple; speak of peace: so
2 For the her - ald's voice is cry - ing in the des - ert
3 Then make straight what long was crook - ed; make the rough - er

says our God. Com - fort those who sit in dark - ness,
far and near, call - ing all to true re - pen - tance,
plac - es plain. Let your hearts be true and hum - ble,

mourn-ing un - der sor-row's load. Cry out to Je - ru - sa - lem
since the king-dom now is here. Oh, that warn-ing cry o - bey!
as be - fits his ho - ly reign. For the glo - ry of the Lord

of the peace that waits for them; tell her that her
Now pre - pare for God a way! Let the val - leys
now on earth is shed a - broad, and all flesh shall

*Words:* Isaiah 40:1-5; versified by Johannes Olearius, 1671; translated by Catherine
Winkworth, 1863
*Music:* Louis Bourgeois, 1551; arranged by Norma de Waal Malefyt, 1992

87 87 77 88
GENEVAN 42

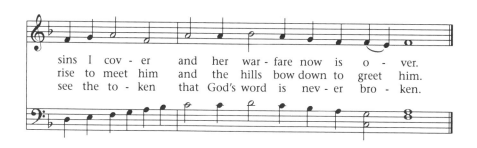

sins I cov - er    and her war - fare now is o - ver.
rise to meet him    and the hills bow down to greet him.
see the to - ken    that God's word is nev - er bro - ken.

## Come, Thou Long-Expected Jesus 122

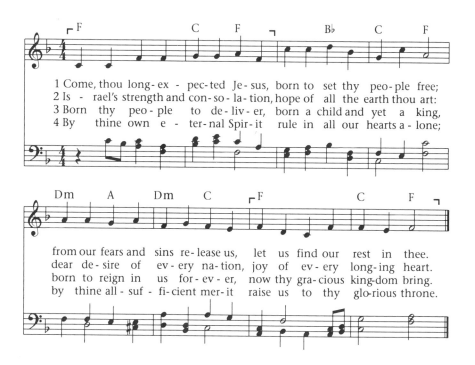

1 Come, thou long - ex - pec - ted Je - sus, born to set thy peo - ple free;
2 Is - rael's strength and con - so - la - tion, hope of all the earth thou art:
3 Born thy peo - ple to de - liv - er, born a child and yet a king,
4 By thine own e - ter - nal Spir - it rule in all our hearts a - lone;

from our fears and sins re - lease us, let us find our rest in thee.
dear de - sire of ev - ery na - tion, joy of ev - ery long-ing heart.
born to reign in us for - ev - er, now thy gra - cious king-dom bring.
by thine all - suf - fi - cient mer - it raise us to thy glo-rious throne.

*Words:* Charles Wesley, 1744
*Music: Psalmodia Sacra*, 1715; adapted by Henry Gauntlett, 1861; arranged by
   Robert Roth, 1989

87 87
STUTTGART
Capo 5

# 123 O Come, O Come, Immanuel

1 O come, O come, Im- man - u - el, and ran - som
2 O come, O Branch of Jes - se's stem, un - to your
3 O come, O Bright and Morn - ing Star, and bring us

cap - tive Is - ra - el that mourns in lone - ly
own and res - cue them! From depths of hell your
com - fort from a - far! Dis - pel the sha - dows

ex - ile here un - til the Son of God ap -
peo - ple save, and give them vic - to - ry o'er the
of the night and turn our dark - ness in - to

*Refrain*

pear.
grave. Re - joice! Re - joice! Im - man - u -
light.

*Words:* Latin, 12th century; composite translation
*Music: Processionale,* 15th century; adapted by Thomas Helmore, 1854;
   arranged by Richard Proulx, 1975; adapted by Robert Roth, 1989

LM with refrain
VENI IMMANUEL

el shall come to you, O Is - ra - el.

*Duet accompaniment (right hand only)
or alternative accompaniment (both hands)*

# 124 Prepare the Way of the Lord

*Canon*

Pre-pare  the  way  of  the  Lord. Pre-pare  the  way  of  the  Lord,

and  all  peo-ple will  see  the  sal - va- tion  of  our  God.  (Pre -)

*Descants*

*(second time)*

*Accompaniment*

For a piano duet, one person plays
the melody an octave higher while
the other person plays this pattern
four times.

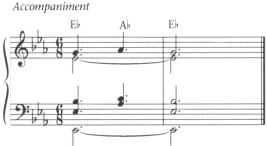

*Words:* Isaiah 40:3; 52:10
*Music:* Jacques Berthier and the Community of Taizé, 1984

Capo 1

# Song of Mary 125

1 My spir - it glo - ri - fies the Lord, in
2 All gen - er - a - tions from now on shall
3 His mer - cy shall ex - tend to those who
4 He brought down rul - ers from their thrones, but
5 He helped his ser - vant Is - ra - el, re -

God my Sav - ior I re - joice, for he be - held my
call me blest and spread my fame, for he has done great
fear the Lord from age to age; he has re - vealed his
lift - ed those of low de - gree. He filled the hun - gry
mem - bering to be mer - ci - ful, keep - ing his word to

hum - ble state and in his love made me his choice.
things for me— might - y and ho - ly is his name.
might - y arm, scat - tering the proud in all their rage.
with good things, but emp - ty sent the rich a - way.
A - bra - ham and to his seed for - ev - er - more.

*Orff instrument pattern*
*Alto xylophone*

*Words:* Luke 1:46-55; versified by Dewey Westra, 1931; revised for *Psalter Hymnal*, 1987
*Music:* Trier manuscript, 15th century; adapted by Michael Praetorius, 1609; arranged
   by Emily R. Brink, 1994

LM
PUER NOBIS

# 126 Stay Awake, Be Ready

1 Stay a - wake, *(clap, clap)* be read - y. You
2 Change your lives, he's com - ing. The

do not know the hour when the Lord is com - ing. Stay a -
one who is the light of the world is com - ing. Change your

wake, be read-y. The Lord is com-ing soon! Al - le -
lives, he's com-ing. The reign of God is near! Al - le -

lu - ia, al - le - lu - ia! The Lord is com - ing soon.
lu - ia, al - le - lu - ia! The reign of God is near.

*Orff instrument patterns*

[Play 3 times]          [Play 3 times]

*Words and Music:* Christopher Walker, 1988

Capo 3

# Look Up! 127

1 Look up! Look up! Look up! See the light of the pro-phets.* Look up! Look up! Look up! See the light of the pro-phets.*

*Refrain*
For the word of the Lord is a light, shin-ing in the dark-ness un-til the Day dawns, and the Morn-ing Star a - ris-es in your hearts.

*2 angels   3 star   4 Jesus

Alto metallophone
Stanzas (play 4x)          Refrain

*Words and Music:* June Fischer Armstrong, based on 2 Peter 1:19
© 1991, CRC Publications.

Capo 5

# 128 The Prophets Came to Israel

1 The proph-ets came to Is-ra-el to tell them what to do. They point-ed to the birth of Christ, and what they said came true, and what they said came true.

2 In Beth-le-hem in a cat-tle stall a mir-a-cle we find: that such a low-ly place should hold the Sav-ior of man-kind, the Sav-ior of man-kind!

3 The shep-herds watched their flocks of sheep when light broke from the sky. They heard a daz-zling an-gel say, "A child is born near-by, a child is born near-by."

4 The angels sang a midnight song,
their eyes were filled with joy:
"the Son of God has come to earth
to be a little boy,
to be a little boy."

5 It's Christmas day! We celebrate
the coming of a king.
He came to set his children free,
and that is why we sing,
and that is why we sing.

*Words and Music:* Bert Witvoet, 1980; harmonized by Bert Polman, 1981

CM with repeat
FIVE CANDLES
Capo 5

# Away in a Manger 129

1 A - way in a man - ger, no crib for a bed,
2 The cat - tle are low - ing, the ba - by a - wakes,
3 Be near me, Lord Je - sus; I ask you to stay

the lit - tle Lord Je - sus laid down his sweet head;
but lit - tle Lord Je - sus, no cry - ing he makes.
close by me for - ev - er and love me, I pray.

the stars in the bright sky looked down where he lay;
I love you, Lord Je - sus: look down from on high
Bless all the dear chil - dren in your ten - der care;

the lit - tle Lord Je - sus a - sleep on the hay.
and stay by my side un - til morn - ing is nigh.
pre - pare us for heav - en to live with you there.

*Words:* American carol, 1885
*Music:* William J. Kirkpatrick, 1895

11 11 11 11
CRADLE SONG
Capo 5

# 130 **That Boy-Child of Mary**

*Refrain* F · · C

That boy-child of Mar - y was born in a sta - ble, a

F · · C⁷ · F

man-ger his cra - dle in Beth - le-hem.

F · · Gm · C · · Am · Dm

1 What shall we call him, child of the man - ger?
2 His name is Je - su, God ev - er with us,
3 He came to save us, he came to help us,

Gm · · C⁷ · F *Repeat refrain*

What name is giv - en in Beth - le - hem?
God giv - en for us in Beth - le - hem.
born here a - mong us in Beth - le - hem.

4 One with the Father, he is our Savior,
   heaven-sent helper of Bethlehem. *Refrain*

5 Gladly we praise him, love and adore him,
   give ourselves to him of Bethlehem. *Refrain*

*Words:* Tom Colvin, 1967
*Music:* Malawian; adapted by Tom Colvin, 1967; arranged by Norma de Waal
  Malefyt, 1992

BLANTYRE
Capo 5

# Go, Tell It on the Mountain 131

**Refrain**

Go, tell it on the moun-tain, o-ver the hills and ev-ery-where;

go, tell it on the moun-tain that Je-sus Christ is born.

1 While shep-herds kept their watch-ing o'er
2 The shep-herds feared and trem-bled when
3 Down in a low-ly sta-ble the

si-lent flocks by night, be-hold, through-out the
lo! a-bove the earth rang out the an-gel
hum-ble Christ was born, and God sent us sal-

heav-ens there shone a ho-ly light.
cho-rus that hailed our Sav-ior's birth.
va-tion that bless-ed Christ-mas morn.

*Repeat refrain*

*Words and Music:* African-American spiritual; arranged by Emily R. Brink, 1991
Arr. © 1994, CRC Publications

76 76 with refrain
GO TELL IT
Capo 5

# 132 Good News

*Words and Music:* Natalie Sleeth, adapted from the anthem "Good News"
© 1980, Hinshaw Music, Inc. Used by permission.

Capo 5

Beth - le - hem's man - ger now cra-dles a King! For there in

B♭  Am  C⁷  F  B♭

un-to us in Beth-le-hem Lord Je-sus is born! For un-to us

a sta - ble Lord Je - sus, our Sav-ior, is born!

Am  Gm  C⁷  F

in Beth-le-hem Lord Je - sus is born!

*Instrumental descant*

# 133 Angels We Have Heard on High

1 An - gels we have heard on high, sing - ing sweet - ly through the night,
2 Shep - herds, why this ju - bi - lee? Why these songs of hap - py cheer?
3 Come to Beth - le - hem and see him whose birth the an - gels sing;

and the moun - tains in re - ply, ech - o - ing their brave de - light.
What great bright - ness did you see? What glad tid - ings did you hear?
come, a - dore on bend - ed knee Christ the Lord, the new - born King.

*Refrain*

Glo - ri - a in ex - cel - sis De - o. Glo - ri - a in ex - cel - sis De - o.

*Words and Music:* French carol, translated by James Chadwick

77 77 with refrain
GLORIA
Capo 5

# Gloria, Gloria 134

Glo - ri - a, glo - ri - a, in ex - cel - sis De - o!

Glo - ri - a, glo - ri - a, al - le - lu - ia, al - le - lu - ia!

*For a piano duet, one person plays only the melody while another person plays this pattern four times:*

Dm   Gm   C   F

*Orff instrument patterns may be created by repeating any of the four patterns of the melody or accompaniment.*

*Flute descants*

*Words:* Luke 2:14; Taizé Community, 1978
*Music:* Jacques Berthier, b. 1923

Capo 5

# 135 Sheep Fast Asleep
## Hitsuji Wa

1 Sheep fast a-sleep, there on a hill, grass for their bed;
2 Star in the sky, shin-ing so bright, si-lent and pure,
3 Glo-ry to God! Glo-ry on high! Sing you "No-el!"

all is still. Cold win-ter night, the frost ap-pears;
won-drous light! What tid-ings brings it Is-ra-el?
Day is nigh! All you who dwell on earth be-low,

shep-herds keep watch by their fire. Soft there a sound,
Can we new hope in it find? Good news it brings!
peace be to you, and good-will. Come, let us go

far, far a-way. Is it the stream? Winds at play? Nay, friend, it
"Fear not, I pray! Born is God's Son, born to-day! God's gift of
to Beth-le-hem; fol-low the star, seek-ing him. Let us a-

*Words:* Japanese hymn by Genzo Miwa, 1907; translated by John Moss, 1957
*Music:* Chugoro Torii, 1941

87 87 87 86
KORIN

is the heaven-ly choir, sing-ing through-out the spheres.
love to all the earth, our Lord, Im-man-u-el."
dore and wor-ship still, in love and joy to grow.

## He Came Down 136

1 He came down that we may have love*; he

came down that we may have love*; he came down that we may

have love.* Hal-le-lu-jah for-ev-er-more. *(Why did he come?)*

* 2 joy  3 peace  4 hope

*Words:* traditional
*Music:* from the Cameroons

# 137 Joy to the World!

1 Joy to the world! The Lord is come: let earth re-
2 Joy to the earth! The Sav - ior reigns: let all their
3 He rules the world with truth and grace, and makes the

ceive her King. Let ev - ery heart pre - pare him
songs em - ploy, while fields and floods, rocks, hills, and
na - tions prove the glo - ries of his right - eous -

room, and heaven and na - ture sing, and heaven and na - ture
plains re - peat the sound-ing joy, re - peat the sound-ing
ness and won-ders of his love, and won-ders of his

sing, and heaven, and heaven and na - ture sing.
joy, re - peat, re - peat the sound-ing joy.
love, and won - ders, won - ders of his love.

*Words:* Isaac Watts, 1719; based on Psalm 98
*Music:* Lowell Mason, 1848

CM with repeats
ANTIOCH

# Come, Lord Jesus 138

1 Come,____ Lord Je - sus, come,____ Lord Je - sus,
2 Come,____ O Prince of Peace, come,____ O Prince of Peace,
3 Our hearts are o - pen, our hearts are o - pen,
4 Come,____ Im - man - u - el, come,____ Im - man - u - el,

come,____ Lord Je - sus:
come,____ O Prince of Peace:
our hearts are o - pen:    come and be born in our hearts.
come,____ Im - man - u - el:

*Words and Music:* Carey Landry

# 139 Huron Carol

1 'Twas in the moon of win - ter - time, when all the
2 With - in a lodge of bro - ken bark the ten - der
3 The ear - liest moon of win - ter - time is not so
4 O chil - dren of the for - est free, the an - gel

birds had fled, that God the Lord of all the earth sent
babe was found; a rag - ged robe of rab - bit skin en -
round and fair as was the ring of glo - ry on the
song is true; the ho - ly Child of earth and heaven is

an - gel choirs in - stead; be - fore their light the
wrapped his beau - ty round; but as the hun - ter
help - less in - fant there. The chiefs from far be -
born to - day for you. Come kneel be - fore the

stars grew dim, and won - dering hun - ters heard the hymn:
braves drew nigh, the an - gel song rang loud and high:
fore him knelt with gifts of fox and bea - ver pelt.
ra - diant boy, who brings you beau - ty, peace, and joy.

*Words:* Jean de Brebeuf (Huron), c. 1643; translated by Jesse Edgar
Middleton, 1926
*Music:* French Canadian

86 86 86 with refrain
JESOUS AHATONHIA

*Refrain*

Je - sus your King is born, Je - sus is

born, in ex - cel - sis glo - ri - a.

*Drum pattern:*

# 140 Child So Lovely
## Niño Lindo

Child so love-ly, here I kneel be-fore you,
Ni - ño lin - do, an - te ti me rin - do,

child so love-ly, you are Christ, my God.
ni - ño lin - do, e - res tú mi Dios.

Child so love-ly, here I kneel be-fore you,
Ni - ño lin - do, an - te ti me rin - do;

child so love-ly, you are Christ, the Lord.
ni - ño lin - do, e - res tú mi Dios.

*Fingertips on palm:*

CARACAS

*Words:* Venezuelan; translated by George Lockwood, 1987
*Music:* Venezuelan melody; arranged by Emily R. Brink, 1993
Trans. © 1989, The United Methodist Publishing House. Arrangement © 1994, CRC Publications.

# Little Baby Jesus 141

1 Lit-tle ba-by Je-sus, born in Beth-le - hem, lit-tle ba-by
2 Lit-tle ba-by Je-sus, born in Beth-le - hem, lit-tle ba-by
3 Lit-tle ba-by Je-sus, born in a sta - ble bare, lit-tle ba-by
4 Lit-tle ba-by Je-sus, born in Beth-le - hem, lit-tle ba-by

Je - sus, born in Beth-le - hem; lit - tle ba-by Je-sus,
Je - sus, born in Beth-le - hem; lit - tle ba-by Je - sus,
Je - sus, ly-ing in a man-ger there; lit - tle ba-by Je - sus,
Je - sus, born in Beth-le - hem; lit - tle ba-by Je - sus,

born to be the Sav-ior of the world for you and me.
born to die; for you and me he came to suf-fer and die.
King to be the Mas-ter of the earth, the sky, and sea.
do come in; come right in - to my heart and save me from sin!

Lit-tle ba-by Je-sus, born in Beth-le - hem.

*Words and Music:* Blaine H. Allen

Capo 3

# 142 What Can I Give Him

What can I give him, poor as I am?

If I were a shep-herd, I would bring a lamb.

If I were a wise man, I would do my part. Yet

what I can I give him— give him my heart.

*Words:* Christina G. Rossetti, 1872; from "In the Bleak Midwinter"
*Music:* Gustav Holst, 1906

Capo 5

# As with Gladness Men of Old 143

1 As with glad-ness men of old did the guid-ing
2 As with joy-ful steps they sped to that low-ly
3 As they of-fered gifts most rare at that cra-dle

star be-hold, as with joy they hailed its light,
in-fant bed, there to bend the knee be-fore
plain and bare, so may we with ho-ly joy,

lead-ing on-ward, beam-ing bright; so, most gra-cious
Christ, whom heaven and earth a-dore; so may we with
pure and free from sin's al-loy, all our cost-liest

Lord, may we ev-er-more your splen-dor see.
will-ing feet ev-er seek your mer-cy seat.
trea-sures bring, Christ, to you, our heav-enly King.

*Words:* William C. Dix, 1860
*Music:* Conrad Kocher, 1838; adapted by William H. Monk, 1861; arranged by
Robert Roth, 1989
Arr. © 1989, Robert Roth

77 77 77
DIX

# 144 When Jesus Saw the Fishermen

*Round*

1 When Jesus saw the fishermen in boats upon the sea,
2 They followed where he healed the sick and gave the hungry bread.
3 And now his friends are everywhere; the circle once so small

he called to them, "Come, leave your nets and follow, follow me."
And others joined them as they went, wherever Jesus led.
extends around the whole wide world, for Jesus calls us all.

*Orff instrument patterns:*

*Bass xylophone*

*Bass metallophone*

*Alto xylophone*

*Alto metallophone*

*Soprano glockenspiel*

*Words:* Edith Agnew, 1953
*Music:* Richard L. Van Oss, 1992

CM
ST. STEPHEN

# Jesus Said to All the People 145

1 Je-sus said to all the peo-ple as they crowd-ed close to
2 Je-sus said to all the peo-ple as he taught them how to

hear, "God loves you as I love you; God is
pray, "God loves you as I love you; God

with you ev-ery - where." Je-sus showed that God
knows the prayers you pray." Je-sus taught that God

loves me; God is with me ev - ery - where.
loves me; God knows the prayers I pray.

*Words:* Ann Evans
*Music:* Swedish folk tune
Arr. © 1972, Graded Press. Used by permission of Abingdon Press.

877 777
JESUS, LAT DIN
Capo 5

# 146 The Good Samaritan

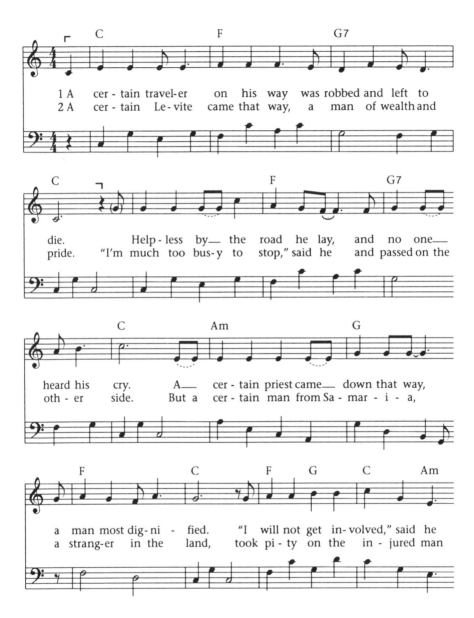

1 A cer-tain travel-er on his way was robbed and left to
2 A cer-tain Le-vite came that way, a man of wealth and

die. Help-less by— the road he lay, and no one—
pride. "I'm much too bus-y to stop," said he and passed on the

heard his cry. A— cer-tain priest came— down that way,
oth-er side. But a cer-tain man from Sa-mar-i-a,

a man most dig-ni-fied. "I will not get in-volved," said he
a strang-er in the land, took pi-ty on the in-jured man

*Words and Music:* Mary Lu Walker, arranged by H. Myron Braun

Reprinted from *Dandelions*, © 1975 by The Missionary Society of St. Paul the Apostle in the State of New York.
Used by permission of Paulist Press.

and passed on the oth- er side. Don't pass your neigh- bor
and lent a—— help- ing hand.

by, my friend; don't pass your neigh - bor by.

Love your neigh- bor as your-self; don't pass your neigh- bor by.

# 147 Four Good Friends

1 Four good friends made a hole in the roof,
four good friends made a hole in the roof,
four good friends made a hole in the roof and
low - ered their friend be - fore Je - sus.

2 "Well, my child, I forgive you your sins" (3x)
 are the words that were spoken by Jesus.

3 "Get off your stretcher and walk, O my son," (3x)
 and he walked, as was told him by Jesus.

4 At that miracle they all were amazed, (3x)
 and they sang many praises to Jesus.

5 Jesus still does his healing today; (3x)
 bring your hurts and your troubles to Jesus.

*Words and Music:* Frank De Vries, 1983; based on Mark 2:3-12
© 1983, CRC Publications

# Jesus' Hands Were Kind Hands 148

1 Je-sus' hands were kind hands, do-ing good to all,
healing pain and sick-ness, bless-ing chil-dren small,
wash-ing ti-red feet and sav-ing those who fall;
Je-sus' hands were kind hands, do-ing good to all.

2 Take my hands, Lord Je-sus, let them work for you;
make them strong and gen-tle, kind in all I do.
Let me watch you, Je-sus, till I'm gen-tle too,
till my hands are kind hands, quick to work for you.

*Words:* Margaret Cropper, c. 1926
*Music:* traditional French melody
Words © Stephan Hopkinson

11 11 11 11
AU CLAIR DE LA LUNE

# 149 When Jesus the Healer

1 When Jesus the healer passed through Galilee,
2 A paralyzed man was let down through a roof.
3 The death of his daughter caused Jairus to weep.
4 When blind Bartimaeus cried out to the Lord,

the deaf came to hear and the blind came to see.
His sins were forgiven, his walking the proof.
The Lord took her hand, and he raised her from sleep.
his faith made him whole and his sight was restored.

*Heal us, heal us today!* ... *Heal us, Lord Jesus!*

5  The lepers were healed and the demons cast out. Heal us, heal us today!
   A bent woman straightened to laugh and to shout. Heal us, Lord Jesus.

6  The twelve were commissioned and sent out in twos, Heal us, heal us today!
   to make the sick whole and to spread the good news. Heal us, Lord Jesus.

7  There's still so much sickness and suffering today. Heal us, heal us today!
   We gather together for healing and pray: Heal us, Lord Jesus.

*Words and Music:* Peter D. Smith, 1979

11 6 11 5
HEALER
Capo 5

# This Is My Commandment 150

*Round*

This is my com-mand-ment, that you love one an-oth-er that your joy may be full. This is my com-mand-ment, that you love one an-oth-er that your joy may be full, that your joy may be full, that your joy may be full.

*Other verses may be added, for example:*

This is my commandment, that you trust one another . . . .
. . . serve one another . . . .
. . . lay down your lives . . . .

*Words:* John 15:11-12·
*Music:* anonymous, arranged by Richard L. Van Oss, 1992
Arr. © 1994, CRC Publications

Capo 1

# 151 If You Love Me

1 If you love me, tru-ly love me, keep my com-mand-ments
2 If you love me, tru-ly love me, come now and my dis-
4 If you love me, tru-ly love me, in-to the world a-

day by day. If you love me, tru-ly love me,
ci - ple be. If you love me, tru-ly love me,
rise and go. If you love me, tru-ly love me,

*Fine*

fol - low for - ev - er in my way.
fol - low and so re - mem - ber me.
there ev - ery-where my wit - ness show.

① Dm                                    ②

3 Through the land my peo - ple feed. Al - le -

*Words and Music:* Natalie Sleeth, based on the anthem "If You Love Me" found in
   the collection *Laudamus*
© 1980, Hinshaw Music, Inc. Used by permission.

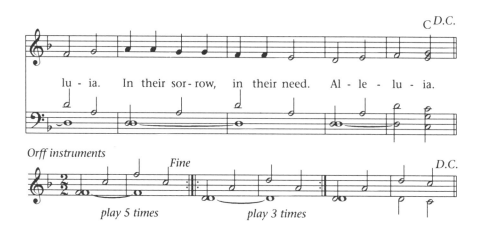

lu - ia.   In their sor - row,   in their need.   Al - le - lu - ia.

*Orff instruments*

*play 5 times*    *play 3 times*

## I Am the Light of the World **152**

I     am the  light of the world,  I  am the   light of the world.   Who-
will nev- er  walk in the dark,  will nev- er   walk in the dark,        but

ev - er  fol - lows me        have  the   light of        life.

*Orff instruments*
*Maracas*

*Words:* John 8:12
*Music:* June Fischer Armstrong, 1991

Capo 1

# 153 Blest Are They

1 Blest are they, the poor in spir-it; theirs is the
2 Blest are they, the low-ly ones; they shall in-
3 Blest are they____ who show mer-cy; mer - cy
4 Blest are they____ who seek peace; they are the

king-dom of God. Blest are they,____
her-it the earth. Blest are they, who
shall be theirs. Blest are they, the
chil-dren of God. Blest are they who

full____ of sor-row; they shall be con-soled.
hun-ger for jus-tice; they shall have their fill.
pure____ of heart; they shall see____ God.
suf-fer ha-tred, all be-cause of me.

*Refrain*
Re-joice and be glad! Bless-ed are you;

*Words:* David Haas, based on Matthew 5:3-12
*Music:* David Haas; arranged by Norma de Waal Malefyt, 1991
© 1985, G.I.A. Publications, Inc. Used by permission.

ho - ly  are you!  Re - joice  and be  glad!

Yours  is  the  king - dom  of  God!  God!

# 154 Bring Forth the Kingdom

1 You are— salt for the earth, O peo-ple: salt for the king-dom of God!
2 You are a light on a hill, O peo-ple: light for the cit-y of God!
3 You are a seed of the Word, O peo-ple: live for the king-dom of God!

share the fla-vor of life, O peo-ple: life in the king-dom of God!
shine so ho-ly and bright,O peo-ple: shine for the king-dom of God!
seeds of mer-cy and seeds of jus-tice, grow in the king-dom of God!

**Refrain**

Bring forth the king-dom of mer-cy; pray for the king-dom of peace;

work for the king-dom of jus-tice; hope for the cit-y of God!

*Words and Music:* Marty Haugen; based on Matt. 5:13-16

# Seek Ye First the Kingdom 155

1 Seek ye— first the king-dom of God and his right-eous-
2 Ask and it shall be giv-en un-to you; seek and you shall
3 We do not live by bread— a - lone, but by ev - ery

ness, and all these things shall be add-ed un-to you.
find; knock and the door shall be o-pened un-to you.
word that pro - ceeds from the mouth— of— God.

*Refrain*

Al - le - lu, al - le - lu - ia. Al - le -

lu - ia, al - le - lu - ia, lu - ia!

*Words:* Matthew 6:33; 7:7; 4:4; adapted by Karen Lafferty, 1972          LAFFERTY
*Music:* Karen Lafferty, 1972; arranged by Robert Roth, 1989

# 156 The King of Glory Comes

*\*Sing small notes as a little descant on the final refrain.*

*Words:* Willard F. Jabusch, 1966
*Music:* Israeli, arranged by John Ferguson, 1973, in *The Hymnal of the United Church of Christ*

12 12 with refrain
PROMISED ONE

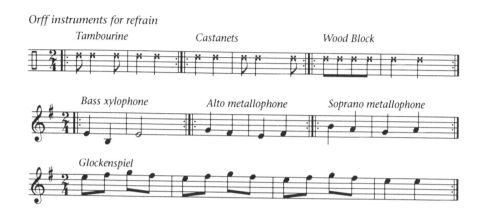

Orff instruments for refrain
Tambourine     Castanets     Wood Block

Bass xylophone     Alto metallophone     Soprano metallophone

Glockenspiel

# Lift Up Your Heads **157**

Lift up your heads, O you gates:
　be lifted up, you ancient doors,
　　that the King of glory may come in.
　　*Refrain (no. 156)*

Who is this King of glory?
　The Lord strong and mighty,
　　the Lord mighty in battle.
　　*Refrain*

Lift up your heads, O you gates;
　Lift them up, you ancient doors,
　　that the King of glory may come in.
　　*Refrain*

Who is he, this King of glory?
　The Lord Almighty—
　　he is the King of glory.
　　*Refrain*

*Words:* Psalm 24:7-10 (NIV)

# 158 Filled with Excitement
## Mantos y Palmos

1 Filled with ex-cite-ment, all the hap-py throng
2 As in that en-trance to Je-ru-sa-lem,

1 Man-tos y pal-mas es-par-cien-do, va
2 Co-mo en la en-tra-da de Je-ru-sa-lén,

spread cloaks and branch-es on the cit-y streets.
we sing ho-san-nas to the Christ, our King,

el pue-blo a-le-gre de Je-ru-sa-lén.
to-dos can-ta-mos a Je-sús el Rey,

There in the dis-tance they be-gin to see,
to the liv-ing Sav-ior who still calls to-day,

A-llá a lo le-jos se em-pie-za a mi-rar
al Cris-to vi-vo que nos lla-ma hoy

rid-ing on a don-key, comes the Son of God.
ask-ing us to fol-low him with love and faith.

en un po-lli-no al Hi-jo de Dios.
pa-ra se-guir-le con a-mor y fe.

*Words:* Rubén Ruiz Avila, 1972; translated by Gertrude C. Suppe, 1979, 1987
*Music:* Rubén Ruiz Avila, 1972; arranged by Alvin Schutmaat

10 10 10 11
with refrain
HOSANNA

Refrain

From ev-ery cor-ner a thou-sand voic-es sing_____ prais-es to him who comes in the name of God. With one great shout of___ ac-cla-ma-tion loud tri-um-phant___ song breaks forth:___ "Ho - san - na! Ho - san - na to the King! Ho - san - na! Ho - san - na to the King!"

Mien-tras mil vo-ces re-sue-nan por do-quier; ho-san-na al que vie-ne en el nom-bre del Se-ñor. Con un a-lien-to de gran ex-cla-ma-ción pro-rrum-pen con voz triun-fal:___ "¡Ho - san - na! ¡Ho - san - na al Rey! ¡Ho - san - na! ¡Ho - san - na al Rey!"

# 159 Trotting, Trotting Through Jerusalem

1 Trot - ting, trot - ting through Je - ru - sa - lem,
Je - sus, sit - ting on a don - key's back; chil - dren wav - ing

*Refrain*

branch - es, sing - ing, "Hap - py is he who
comes in the name of the Lord!"

*Final ending*

*Words and Music:* Eric Reid, 1936-1970

Capo 5

2 Many people in Jerusalem
   thought he should have come on a mighty horse
   leading all the Jews to battle— *Refrain*

3 Many people in Jerusalem
   were amazed to see such a quiet man
   trotting, trotting on a donkey— *Refrain*

4 Trotting, trotting through Jerusalem,
   Jesus, sitting on a donkey's back;
   let us join the children, singing, *Refrain*

*Xylophone*

# 160 Hosanna! Hosanna!

"Ho - san - na! Ho - san - na!" the lit - tle chil - dren sing; "Ho - san - na! Ho - san - na! For Christ, our Lord, is King." "Pre - pare the way," the chil - dren sing, "Ho - san - na to our Lord and King!"

*Words and Music:* Helen Kemp

Reprinted by permission from *Let's Sing*, © 1988, Augsburg Fortress

Capo 1

# All Glory, Laud, and Honor 161

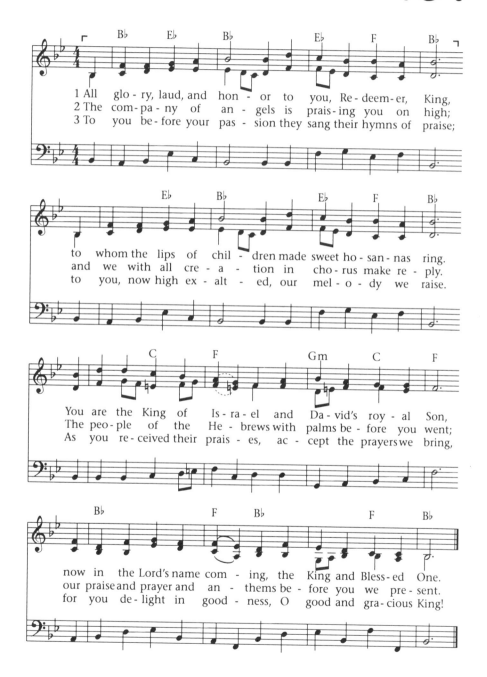

1 All glo - ry, laud, and hon - or to you, Re - deem - er, King,
2 The com - pa - ny of an - gels is prais - ing you on high;
3 To you be - fore your pas - sion they sang their hymns of praise;

to whom the lips of chil - dren made sweet ho - san - nas ring.
and we with all cre - a - tion in cho - rus make re - ply.
to you, now high ex - alt - ed, our mel - o - dy we raise.

You are the King of Is - ra - el and Da - vid's roy - al Son,
The peo - ple of the He - brews with palms be - fore you went;
As you re - ceived their prais - es, ac - cept the prayers we bring,

now in the Lord's name com - ing, the King and Bless - ed One.
our praise and prayer and an - thems be - fore you we pre - sent.
for you de - light in good - ness, O good and gra - cious King!

*Words:* Theodulph of Orleans, c. 820; translated by John M. Neale, 1851
*Music:* Melchior Teschner, 1615; harmonized by William H. Monk, 1861

76 76 D
ST. THEODULPH
Capo 3

# 162 Hosanna, Son of David!

Ho - san - na, son of Da - vid! Bless-ed be his
ho - ly name. Glo - ry to the Son of Da - vid,
who comes in the name of the Lord. Sing ho -san - na
Ho - san - in the high - est, sing ho - san - na, ho - san - na.
na, ho - san - na. Glo-ry
to the Son of Da - vid, who comes in the name of the Lord.

*Words and Music:* G. J. Vogler (1749-1814), based on Matthew 21:9; translated by
   J. Irving Erickson (1914-1992)

# Oh, How He Loves You and Me 163

1 Oh, how he loves you and me. Oh, how he
loves you and me. He gave his life— what
more could he give? Oh, how he loves you;
oh, how he loves me; oh, how he loves you and me!

2 Je - sus to Cal - vary did go,
love for all peo - ple to show;
what he did there brought hope from de - spair.

*Words and Music:* Kurt Kaiser

# 164 Part of the Plan

1 'Twas all part of the plan, since first the world be-
2 'Twas all des-tined to be by God's di-vine de-
4 So come now and be glad! Why should your heart be

gan: that on the tree he died for me. 'Twas
cree: his life he gave, our souls to save. 'Twas
sad? For God's own Son the vic-tory won. 'Twas

all des-tined to be!
all des-tined to be! 3 For God or-dained from
all part of the plan.

long a-go that Christ the Lord should suf-fer so, that

*Words and Music:* Natalie Sleeth, based on the anthem "Part of the Plan"
© 1976, Hinshaw Music, Inc. Used by permission.

by his death the world would know the glo - ry of his ris - ing!

# 165 As Moses Raised the Serpent Up

Canon

1 As Moses raised the serpent up,
2 For God so loved the world he made,
3 God did not send Christ to the world
4 For God so loved the world he made,

so must God's Son be lift-ed high,
he gave his own be-lov-ed Son;
that he might then con-demn us all,
he gave his own be-lov-ed Son;

that who-so-ev - er will be-lieve
all who be-lieve in him will live—
but that the world by Christ's own death
all who be-lieve in him will live—

in him may live e-ter-nal-ly.
not die, but live for-ev-er-more.
might then be ran - somed from the fall.
not die, but live for-ev-er-more.

*Words:* John 3:14-17; versified by Marie J. Post, 1985
*Music:* English folk tune; arranged by Hal Hopson, 1972

LM
GIFT OF LOVE

# When I Survey the Wondrous Cross 166

1 When I sur - vey the won - drous cross
2 For - bid it, Lord, that I should boast
3 See, from his head, his hands, his feet,
4 Were the whole realm of na - ture mine,

on which the Prince of glo - ry died,
save in the death of Christ, my God!
sor - row and love flow min - gled down.
that were a pres - ent far too small.

my rich - est gain I count but loss,
All the vain things that charm me most,
Did e'er such love and sor - row meet,
Love so a - maz - ing, so di - vine,

and pour con - tempt on all my pride.
I sac - ri - fice them through his blood.
or thorns com - pose so rich a crown?
de - mands my soul, my life, my all.

*Words:* Isaac Watts, 1707
*Music:* Lowell Mason, 1824

LM
HAMBURG
Capo 5

# 167 Were You There

1 Were you there when they cru-ci-fied my Lord? Were you there when they cru-ci-fied my Lord? Oh, some-times it caus-es me to trem-ble, trem-ble, trem-ble. Were you there when they cru-ci-fied my Lord?

2 Were you there when they nailed him to the tree? . . .
3 Were you there when they laid him in the tomb? . . .
4 Were you there when God raised him from the tomb? . . .

*Words and Music:* African-American spiritual

10 10 14 10
WERE YOU THERE
Capo 1

## Jesus, Remember Me  168

*Words:* Luke 23:42
*Music:* Jacques Berthier, 1978

JESUS, REMEMBER ME
Capo 1

# 169 What Wondrous Love Is This

1 What won-drous love is this, O my soul, O my soul!
2 When I was sink-ing down, sink-ing down, sink-ing down,
3 To God and to the Lamb I will sing, I will sing,
4 And when from death I'm free, I'll sing on, I'll sing on,

What won-drous love is this, O my soul!
when I was sink-ing down, sink-ing down;
to God and to the Lamb I will sing;
and when from death I'm free, I'll sing on;

What won-drous love is this that caused the Lord of bliss
when I was sink-ing down be - neath God's right-eous frown,
to God and to the Lamb, who is the great I AM—
and when from death I'm free, I'll sing and joy - ful be,

to bear the dread-ful curse for my soul, for my soul,
Christ laid a - side his crown for my soul, for my soul,
while mil - lions join the theme, I will sing, I will sing,
and through e - ter - ni - ty I'll sing on, I'll sing on,

*Words: S. Mead's A General Selection, 1811*
*Music: W. Walker's Southern Harmony, 1835; harmonized by*
    Richard L. Van Oss, 1992
Harm. © 1994, CRC Publications

12 9 12 12 9
WONDROUS LOVE
Capo 5

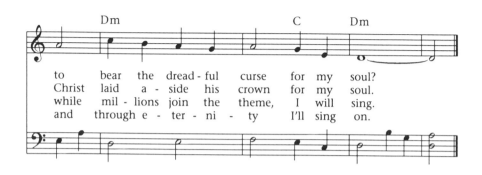

to       bear   the   dread-ful   curse   for   my   soul?
Christ   laid   a - side   his   crown   for   my   soul.
while   mil - lions join   the   theme,   I   will   sing.
and   through e - ter - ni - ty   I'll   sing   on.

## Worthy Is Christ
## Digno Es Jesús  **170**

1 Wor - thy   is   Christ,   wor - thy   is   Christ;
2 He   gave   his   life,   he   died   for   me;
1 Dig - no es Je - sús,   dig - no es Je - sús;
2 Su   vi - da   dio,   por   mí   mu - rió;

to   him   be praise and glo - ry:   wor - thy   is   the Lord.
de   re - ci - bir   la glo - ria,   dig - no   es   Je - sús.

*Words and Music:* traditional Spanish

DIGNO ES JESUS
Capo 5

# 171 Lift High the Cross

*Refrain*

Lift high the cross, the love of Christ pro - claim
till all the world a - dore his sa - cred name.

1 Come, Chris - tians, fol - low where our Sav - ior led,
2 All new - born ser - vants of the Cru - ci - fied
3 O Lord, once lift - ed on the tree of pain,
4 Let ev - ery race and ev - ery lan - guage tell

our King vic - to - rious, Je - sus Christ, our Head.
bear on their brows the seal of him who died.
draw all the world to seek you once a - gain.
of him who saves our lives from death and hell.

*Words* George W. Kitchin, 1887; revised by Michael R. Newbolt, 1916
*Music:* Sydney H. Nicholson, 1916; arranged by Robert Roth

10 10 with refrain
CRUCIFER

# Christ the Lord Is Risen Today 172

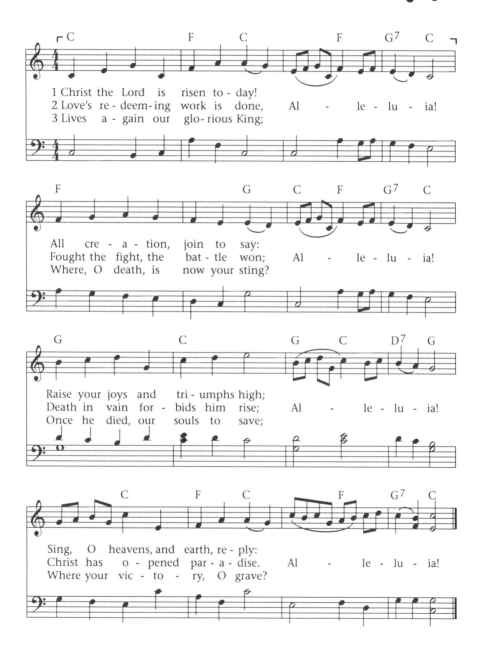

1 Christ the Lord is risen to-day!
2 Love's re-deem-ing work is done, Al - le - lu - ia!
3 Lives a - gain our glo-rious King;

All cre - a - tion, join to say:
Fought the fight, the bat - tle won; Al - le - lu - ia!
Where, O death, is now your sting?

Raise your joys and tri - umphs high;
Death in vain for - bids him rise; Al - le - lu - ia!
Once he died, our souls to save;

Sing, O heavens, and earth, re - ply:
Christ has o - pened par - a - dise. Al - le - lu - ia!
Where your vic - to - ry, O grave?

*Words:* Charles Wesley, 1739
*Music: Lyra Davidica,* 1708; arranged by Emily R. Brink, 1993
Arr. © 1994, CRC Publications

77 77 with alleluias
EASTER HYMN

# 173 Alleluia, Alleluia! Give Thanks

*Refrain*

Al - le - lu - ia, al - le - lu - ia! Give thanks to the ris - en Lord.

Al - le - lu - ia, al - le - lu - ia! Give praise to his name.

1 Je - sus is Lord of all the earth;
2 Spread the good news o'er all the earth:
3 We have been cru - ci - fied with Christ;
4 Come, let us praise the liv - ing God,

he is the King of cre - a - tion.
Je - sus has died and has ris - en.
now we shall live___ for - ev - er.
joy - ful - ly sing to our Sav - ior.

*Words and Music:* Donald Fishel, 1971; arranged by Emily R. Brink, 1993;
descant by Roy Hopp, 1993

CHURCH STREET
Capo 5

*Descant*

*Fine*

*D.C.*

## He's Alive! 174

*Round* ① G    D⁷    G ②

The Lord is ris-en from the dead. The Lord is ris-en,

D⁷    G ③    D⁷    *Final ending G*

as he said. He's a-live! He's a-live! He's a-live!

*After group ③ is finished, everyone sings the final ending together.*

*Orff instruments*

Bass xylophone    Alto xylophone

Alto glockenspiel    Soprano glockenspiel

*Words and Music:* Tom Fettke; arranged by Richard L. Van Oss, 1992

# 175 This Is the Day

This is the day that the Lord has made! Re - joice! Re -
joice, and be ex - ceed - ing glad! This is the day that the Lord has
made! Re - joice! Re - joice! Hal - le - lu - jah!

1 Christ has con - quered death at last. Left the tomb that held him fast! Gone the
2 Je - sus lives who once was dead! Crown of glo - ry on his head. Ri - sen

sor - row, gone the night. Dawns the morning clear and bright!
now our Lord and King. Songs of glad - ness

*Words and Music:* Natalie Sleeth, adapted from the anthem "This Is the Day"
© 1976, Hinshaw Music, Inc. Used by permission.

Capo 5

# 176 Come and See

Leader    C           F/C    C    All    G

1 The night was dark and filled with gloom.
2 Then sud-den-ly the Lord ap-peared (Come and see!
3 Well, Thom-as said, "My God, my Lord!"

C       F  Leader C           Am      Em

            They hid with-in a se-cret room.
Come and   see.) to see his friends and calm their fears.
            Now I be-lieve the liv-ing Word.

All F       C    G⁷      C    Leader

            Now Thom-as had not
(Come and   see!  Come and see.) To Thom-as he said,
                  Go tell the peo-ple

F       C    All    G    C    F    Leader

seen the Lord.                           He
"See my hand."  (Come and see!  Come and see.)  It
far and wide,                            'twas

*Words:* John Ylvisaker, based on John 20:24-28
*Music:* African-American spiritual

doubt - ed  ev - ery  sin - gle  word.
hap - pened  just  as  God  had  planned. (Come and  see!
for  their  sins  that  Je - sus  died.

*Refrain*

Come and  see.)  I  be - lieve  this  is  Je - sus!

Come and  see!  Come and  see.  Oh,  I  be - lieve

this  is  Je - sus!  Come and  see!  Come and  see.

# 177 Oh, How Good Is Christ the Lord
## Oh, Qué Bueno Es Jesús

Oh, how good is Christ the Lord! On the cross he
Oh, qué bue - no es Je - sús. Que por mí mu -

died for me. He has par - doned all my sin, Glo - ry be to
rió en la cruz. Mis pe - ca - dos per - do - nó. A su nom - bre

Je - sus. Glo - ry be to Je - sus! Glo - ry be to Je - sus!
glo - ria. A su nom - bre glo - ria. A su nom - bre glo - ria.

In three days he rose a - gain. Glo - ry be to Je - sus.
En tres días re - su - ci - tó. A su nom - bre glo - ria.

*Words and Music:* Puerto Rican folk hymn; harmonized by Dale Grotenhuis, 1985    OH QUE BUENO
Harm. © 1987, CRC Publications

## He Is Lord 178

1 He is Lord, he is Lord, he is ris - en from the
dead, and he is Lord! Ev - ery knee shall bow, ev - ery
tongue con - fess that Je - sus Christ is Lord.

2 He is King, he is King, he will draw all na - tions
to him; he is King! And the time shall be when the
world shall sing that Je - sus Christ is King.

3 He is Love, he is Love,
   he has shown us by his life that he is Love!
   All his people sing with one voice of joy
   that Jesus Christ is Love.

4 He is Life, he is Life,
   he has died to set us free, and he is Life!
   And he calls us all to live evermore,
   for Jesus Christ is Life.

*Words:* anonymous, based on Philippians 2:10-11; John 12:32
*Music:* anonymous, harmonized by Dale Grotenhuis, 1986
Harm. © 1987, CRC Publications

HE IS LORD
Capo 3

# 179 Clap Your Hands

*Round* ①

1 Clap your hands, all you peo - ple; shout un - to God with a
2 Clap your hands, all you peo - ple; Christ has as - cend - ed

voice of tri - umph! Clap your hands, all you peo - ple;
in - to hea - ven! Clap your hands, all you peo - ple;

shout un - to God with a voice of praise! Ho - san - na! Ho -
Christ has as - cend - ed with shouts of joy! Ho - san - na! Ho -

san - na! Shout un - to God with a voice of tri - umph!
san - na! Christ has as - cend - ed in - to hea - ven!

④ Praise him! Praise him! Shout un - to God with a voice of praise!
Praise him! Praise him! Christ has as - cend - ed with shouts of joy!

*Words:* stanza 1, Psalm 47:1, paraphrase by Jimmy Owens, 1972;
stanza 2, Bert Polman, 1991
*Music:* Jimmy Owens, 1972; harmonized by Charlotte Larsen, 1991

CLAP YOUR HANDS

# Rejoice, the Lord Is King 180

1 Re - joice, the Lord is King! Your Lord and King a - dore.
2 His king-dom can - not fail; he rules o'er earth and heaven;
3 He sits at God's right hand till all his foes sub - mit,
4 Re - joice in glo - rious hope; for Christ, the Judge, shall come

Re - joice, give thanks and sing and tri - umph ev - er - more.
the keys of death and hell to Christ the Lord are given.
bow down at his com - mand, and fall be - neath his feet.
to gath - er all his saints to their e - ter - nal home.

Lift up your heart, lift up your voice.
Lift up your heart, lift up your voice.
Lift up your heart, lift up your voice.
We soon shall hear the arch - an - gel's voice;

Re - joice, a - gain I say, re - joice!
Re - joice, a - gain I say, re - joice!
Re - joice, a - gain I say, re - joice!
the trump of God shall sound, re - joice!

*Words:* Charles Wesley, 1744
*Music:* John Darwall, 1770; harmonized by Charlotte Larsen, 1992
Harm. © 1994, CRC Publications

66 66 88
DARWALL'S 148th

# 181 Crown Him with Many Crowns

3 Crown him the Lord of peace; his king - dom is at

D          G          D

1 Crown him with man - y crowns, the Lamb up - on his
2 Crown him the Lord of life, tri - um - phant o'er the
3 Crown him the Lord of peace; his king - dom is at

hand. From pole to pole let war - fare cease and

A          D          E          A

throne, while heaven's e - ter - nal an - them drowns all
grave, who rose vic - to - rious from the strife for
hand. From pole to pole let war - fare cease and

Christ rule ev - ery land! All hail, Re - deem - er,

E          A          D

mu - sic but its own! A - wake, my soul, and
those he came to save. His glo - ries now we
Christ rule ev - ery land! All hail, Re - deem - er,

*Words:* Stanzas 1, 3, Matthew Bridges, 1851; stanza 2, Godfrey Thring, 1874
*Music:* George J. Elvey, 1868; descant Hal H. Hopson, 1979

SMD
DIADEMATA

hail, for you died for me. Crown him Lord

G      E      A      D

sing      of    him  who  died  to  be      your  Sav - ior
sing     who  died  and  reigns  on  high;    he  died,  e -
hail,    for  you  have  died  for  me.    Your  praise  shall

of  love      through - out  e - ter - ni - ty.

A    D      A    D

and  your  match - less  King  through  all    e - ter - ni - ty.
ter - nal  life  to  bring,  and  lives  that  death  may  die.
nev - er,  nev - er  fail  through - out  e - ter - ni - ty.

# 182 On the First Pentecost

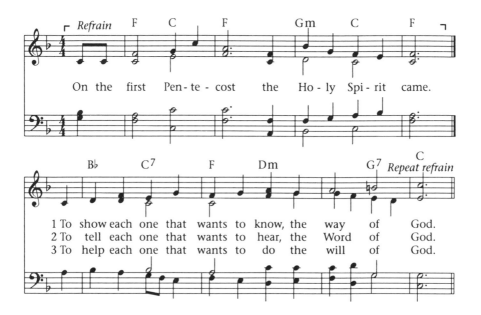

On the first Pen-te-cost the Ho-ly Spi-rit came.

1 To show each one that wants to know, the way of God.
2 To tell each one that wants to hear, the Word of God.
3 To help each one that wants to do the will of God.

*Words:* Coby Veenstra
*Music:* Norma de Waal Malefyt, 1992
© 1994, CRC Publications

Capo 5

# O Holy Spirit, Breathe on Me  183

1 O Ho-ly Spir - it, breathe on me,
2 O Ho-ly Spir - it, fill my life,
3 O Ho-ly Spir - it, make me new,
4 O Ho-ly Spir - it, wind of God,

O Ho-ly Spir - it, breathe on me,
O Ho-ly Spir - it, fill my life,
O Ho-ly Spir - it, make me new,
O Ho-ly Spir - it, wind of God,

and wash a - way my sin, fill me with love with-in:
take all my pride from me, give me hu - mil - i - ty:
make Je - sus real to me, give me his pu - ri - ty:
give me your power to - day, to live in you al - ways:

*Final ending*

O Ho-ly Spir - it, breathe on me.

*Words and Music:* Norman Warren, 1980; arranged by Emily R. Brink, 1994

Capo 5

# 184 Spirit of the Living God

1 Spir-it of the liv-ing God, fall a-fresh on me;
2 Spir-it of the liv-ing God, move a-mong us all;

Spir-it of the liv-ing God, fall a-fresh on me.
make us one in heart and mind, make us one in love;

Melt me, mold me, fill me, use me.
hum - ble, car - ing, self - less, shar - ing.

Spir-it of the liv-ing God, fall a-fresh on me.
Spir-it of the liv-ing God, fill our lives with love.

*Words:* stanza 1, Daniel Iverson, 1926: stanza 2, Michael Baughen, 1982
*Music:* Daniel Iverson, 1926

IVERSON
Capo 1

# Spirit Divine, Inspire Our Prayer 185

1 Spir - it di - vine, in - spire our prayer and make our
2 Come as the light; re - veal our need, our hid - den
3 Come as the fire and cleanse our hearts with pu - ri -
4 Come as the dove and spread your wings, the wings of

hearts your home; de - scend with all your
fail - ings show, and lead us in those
fy - ing flame; let our whole life an
peace and love, un - til your church on

gra - cious power; come, Ho - ly Spir - it, come!
paths of life where - on the right - eous go.
of - fering be to our Re - deem - er's name.
earth be - low joins with your church a - bove.

*Words:* Andrew Reed, 1829, alt.
*Music:* Johann Crüger, 1647; harmonized by Bert Polman, 1994
Harm. © 1994, CRC Publications

CM
GRAFENBERG
Capo 3

# 186 Now Holy Spirit, Ever One

Now Ho - ly Spir - it, ev - er one
with God the Fa - ther and the Son,
pour forth in - to our hearts, we pray,
the full - ness of your grace to - day.

*Words:* Ambrose of Milan; versified in *Hymnal 1982*
*Music:* William Knapp, 1738; harmonized by Emily R. Brink, 1994
Harm. © 1994, CRC Publications

LM
WAREHAM

# The Spirit of the Lord 187

*with hand drum beating quarter notes throughout*

The Spir-it of the Lord fills the world! Al-le-lu-ia!

The Spir-it of the Lord fills the world! Al-le-lu-ia!

The Spir-it of the Lord fills the world! Al-le-lu-ia!

(Group 1) Come, Ho-ly Spir-it. Come, Ho-ly Spir-it.

*(continue as ostinato, until the beginning of the last line)*

(Group 2) Fill the hearts of the faith-ful!

(Group 3) Kin-dle in them the fire of love!

(All) Let the right-eous re-joice be-fore God! Al-le-lu-ia!

*Words:* Based on the Introit and Gradual for Pentecost
*Music:* Betty Ann Ramseth

# 188 The Fruit of the Spirit

For the fruit of the Spir-it is love, joy, peace, pa-tience, kind-ness, good - ness, faith-ful-ness, gen-tle-ness, self - con - trol; for such there is no law.

*Words:* Galatians 5:22-23
*Music:* Brian C. Casebow
© Brian C. Casebow. Used by permission.

Capo 1

# 189 I'm Gonna Sing

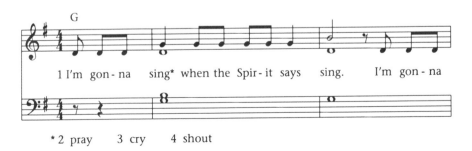

1 I'm gon-na sing* when the Spir-it says sing. I'm gon-na

*2 pray    3 cry    4 shout

*Words and Music:* African-American spiritual

sing when the Spir-it says sing. I'm gon-na sing when the

Spir-it says sing, and o-bey the Spir-it of the Lord.

## Walk! Walk! 190

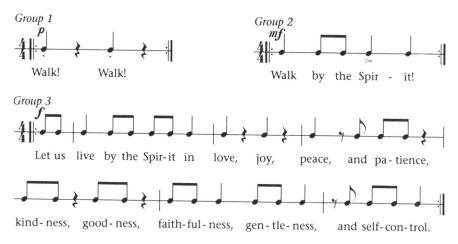

*Group 1*

Walk! Walk!

*Group 2*

Walk by the Spir - it!

*Group 3*

Let us live by the Spir-it in love, joy, peace, and pa-tience,

kind-ness, good-ness, faith-ful-ness, gen-tle-ness, and self-con-trol.

*For a processional, one child leads the choir in, single-file, establishing the beat with a wood-block. Group 1 follows, speaking four measures before group 2 begins to speak. Group 3 begins four measures later and can repeat its passage as groups 1 and 2 quietly accompany. Then group 2 drops out, and finally group 1.*

*Words:* Galatians 5:22-23,25
*Music:* Betty Ann Ramseth, 1970

Reprinted from *That I May Speak,* © 1970, Augsburg Publishing House. Used by permission of Augsburg Fortress.

# 191 Like the Murmur of the Dove's Song

1 Like the mur - mur of the dove's song, like the
2 To the mem - bers of Christ's bod - y, to the
3 With the heal - ing of di - vi - sion, with the

chal - lenge of her flight, like the vig - or of the
branch - es of the Vine, to the church in faith as -
cease - less voice of prayer, with the power to love and

wind's rush, like the new flame's ea - ger might:
sem - bled, to her midst as gift and sign:
wit - ness, with the peace be - yond com - pare:

Come, Ho - ly Spir - it, come.
Come, Ho - ly Spir - it, come.
Come, Ho - ly Spir - it, come.

*Words:* Carl P. Daw, Jr., 1981
*Music:* Peter Cutts, 1968
Words © 1982, music © 1969, Hope Publishing Co. All rights reserved. Used by permission.

87 87 6
BRIDEGROOM
Capo 3

# There's a Spirit in the Air 192

1 There's a spirit in the air, telling Christians
2 Lose your shyness, find your tongue, tell the world what
3 When believers break the bread, when a hungry

ev - ery - where: "Praise the love that Christ re - vealed,
God has done: God in Christ has come to stay.
child is fed, praise the love that Christ re - vealed,

liv - ing, work - ing in our world."
Live to - mor - row's life to - day!
liv - ing, work - ing in our world.

4 When a stranger's not alone,
where the homeless find a home,
praise the love that Christ revealed,
living, working in our world.

5 May the Spirit fill our praise,
guide our thoughts and change our ways.
God in Christ has come to stay.
Live tomorrow's life today!

*Words:* Brian Wren, 1969, revised 1987
*Music:* John W. Wilson, 1967

77 77
LAUDS

# 193 Alabaré

*Words:* Spanish words by Manuel José Alonso; English words by
Bert Polman, 1986; based on Revelation 5:11-14
*Music:* José Pagán

11 10 10 10 with refrain
ALABARE

heard the song they sing to praise the Lamb.
praise the Lamb who gave his life for us:
peat the cho - rus, prais - ing God in song:

Thou - sands are pray - ing, mil - lions are sing - ing; a -
pow - er and glo - ry, wis - dom and hon - or be
bless - ing and hon - or, glo - ry and pow - er be

loud they raise their voice to praise the Lamb.
to the Lamb who gave his life for us.
to the Lord for - ev - er - more, A - men!

*Repeat refrain*

*Spanish words:*
1 Juan vio el número     de los redimidos,     y todos alababan al Señor.
  Unos oraban,           otros cantaban,       y todos alababan al Señor.

2 Todos unidos           alegres cantemos      gloria y alabanzas al Señor.
  Gloria al Padre,       gloria al Hijo,        y gloria al Espíritu de amor.

3 Somos tus hijos,       Dios Padre eterno,     Tú nos has creado por amor.
  Te adoramus,           te benedecimos,        y todos cantamos en tu honor.

# 194. Soon and Very Soon

1 Soon and ver - y soon we are going to see the King;

soon and ver - y soon we are going to see the King;

soon and ver - y soon we are going to see the King.

Hal-le - lu - jah! Hal-le - lu - jah! We're going to see the King.

2 No more dying there . . . .
3 No more crying there . . . .

*Words and Music:* Andraé Crouch, 1978; music adapted by William Farley Smith, 1987

VERY SOON
Capo 3

# For All the Saints 195

1 For all the saints who from their la - bors rest,
2 May all your sol - diers, faith - ful, true, and bold,
3 O blest com - mu - nion, fel - low - ship di - vine!

who to the world by faith their Lord con - fessed,
fight as the saints who no - bly fought of old,
We feeb - ly strug - gle, they in glo - ry shine;

your name, O Je - sus, be for - ev - er blest.
and win with them the vic - tor's crown of gold.
yet all are one with - in your great de - sign.

Al - le - lu - ia, al - le - lu - ia!

*Words:* William W. How, 1864
*Music:* Ralph Vaughan Williams, 1906
Used by permission of Oxford University Press, London.

10 10 10 with alleluias
SINE NOMINE

# 196 The Trees of the Field

1 You shall go out with joy and be led forth with peace;
2 The fir and cy - press trees will grow in - stead of thorns:

the moun - tains and the hills will break forth be -
the myr - tle will re - place the bri - ars and

fore you; there'll be shouts of joy, and all the trees of the
net - tles: this will be a sign, a sign of God's might - y

field will clap, will clap their hands!
name, that will not be de - stroyed.

*Words:* Isaiah 55:12-13; st. 1 by Steffi Karen Rubin, 1975; st. 2 by Bert Polman, 1985
*Music:* Stuart Dauermann, 1975

# 197 Swing Low, Sweet Chariot

*Refrain*

Swing low, sweet char-i-ot, com-ing for to car-ry me home;
swing low, sweet char-i-ot, com-ing for to car-ry me home.

1 I looked o-ver Jor-dan, and what did I see,
2 If you get there be-fore I do—
3 Some-times I'm up, some-times I'm down—

com-ing for to car-ry me home? A band of an-gels
com-ing for to car-ry me home— tell all my friends I'm
com-ing for to car-ry me home— but still I know I'm

*Words and Music:* African-American spiritual

SWING LOW
Capo 5

com-ing af-ter me, com-ing for to car-ry me home.
com-ing there too— com-ing for to car-ry me home.
heav-en-ward bound— com-ing for to car-ry me home.

# Living in God's World

# 198 He's Got the Whole World

1 He's got the whole world in his hands. He's got the whole world in his hands. He's got the whole world in his hands. He's got the whole world in his hands.

2 He's got the little tiny baby in his hands. (3x)
He's got the whole world in his hands.

3 He's got you and me, brother, in his hands. . . .

4 He's got you and me, sister, in his hands. . . .

5 He's got everybody here in his hands. . . .

*Words and Music:* African-American spiritual

WHOLE WORLD

# All Night, All Day 199

All night, all day, an-gels watch-ing o-ver me, my Lord.

All night, all day, an-gels watch-ing o-ver me.

1 Now I lay me down to sleep.
2 Lord, stay with me through the night. An-gels watching o-ver me, my Lord.

Pray the Lord my soul to keep.
Wake me with the morn-ing light. An-gels watch-ing o-ver me.

*Words and Music:* spiritual

# 200 The Lord Is My Shepherd

*Round* (1)

The Lord is my shep-herd; I'll walk with him al - ways. He

leads me by still wa - ters; I'll walk with him al - ways. *Fine*

(2)

Al - ways, al - ways, I'll walk with him al - ways. Al -

ways, al - ways, I'll walk with him al - ways. *D.C.*

*Alternative words: "I'll follow him," or "I'll live for him"*

*Second piano part, for playing as a duet:*

*Repeat through the entire song.*
*May also be played on Orff instruments.*

*Words:* Psalm 23:1-2
*Music:* folk melody; arranged by Charlotte Larsen, 1992
Arr. © 1994, CRC Publications

Capo 3

# The Lord, My Shepherd 201

1 The Lord, my shep-herd, rules my life and
2 The Lord re-vives my fail-ing strength, he
3 Though in a val-ley dark as death, no

gives me all I need; he leads me by re-
makes my joy com-plete; and in right paths, for
e-vil makes me fear; your shep-herd's staff pro-

fresh-ing streams; in pas-tures green I feed.
his name's sake, he guides my fal-tering feet.
tects my way, for you are with me there.

4 While all my enemies look on,
　you spread a royal feast;
　you fill my cup, anoint my head,
　and treat me as your guest.

5 Your goodness and your gracious love
　pursue me all my days;
　your house, O Lord, shall be my home—
　your name, my endless praise.

*Duet accompaniment*

*optional*

*Words:* Psalm 23; versified by Christopher M. Idle, 1977
*Music:* Jessie Seymour Irvine, 1872; arranged by Richard L. Van Oss, 1991

CM
CRIMOND
Capo 3

# 202 This Is How We Know

*Words:* 1 John 3:16 (NIV)
*Music:* Frank Hernandez, 1990; arranged by Norma de Waal Malefyt, 1992

down his life    for us,    for

Dm          G [1]
for us,    for us,    for

[2]
us,    for us,    for us.

C          [2]
us.    us,    for us.

# 203 You Are Our God; We Are Your People

1 It rained on the earth for-ty days, for-ty nights,
2 God told A-bra-ham, "I will give you a land,
3 And when Je-sus Christ came to live on the earth,
4 To us and our chil-dren the pro-mise is made,

and all of the world was de-stroyed. The ark No-ah
a peo-ple as man-y as the stars." Though child-less and
God's pro-mise to us was ful-filled. His life and his
if we will but trust in his word. In bap-tism

built at the call-ing of God saved God's cho-sen
old, he and Sar-ah be-lieved and trust-ed the
death were a new cov-e-nant, as-sur-ance of
join-ing the peo-ple of God, we live in the

ones from the flood. God gave to No-ah the
word of the Lord. God gave them I-saac, a
love full and free. God gave his Son, his
power of his grace. God gives us life, and we

*Words and Music: David A. Hoekema, 1978*
© 1985, CRC Publications

JANNA

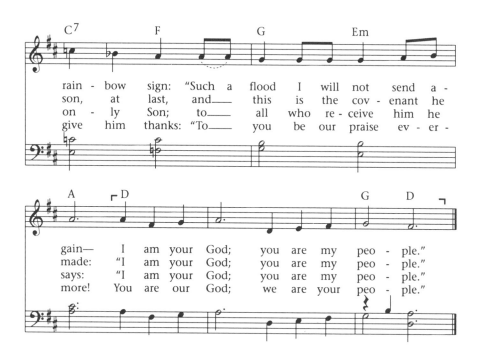

| | | | | |
|---|---|---|---|---|
| rain - bow | sign: | "Such a | flood | I will not send a - |
| son, | at last, | and___ | this | is the cov - enant he |
| on - ly | Son; | to___ | all | who re - ceive him he |
| give him | thanks: | "To___ | you | be our praise ev - er - |

| | | | |
|---|---|---|---|
| gain— | I am your God; | you are my | peo - ple." |
| made: | "I am your God; | you are my | peo - ple." |
| says: | "I am your God; | you are my | peo - ple." |
| more! | You are our God; | we are your | peo - ple." |

# 204 Love Is Never Ending

1 We give thanks un-to you, O God of might,
2 From of old you have led your peo - ple in faith,
3 You de - liv - ered the ones who called un - to you,
4 You have o - pened the sea and brought your peo - ple through,
5 You re - mem - ber your prom - ise age to age,

for your love is nev - er - end - ing;

we give thanks un - to you, the God of gods,
you have shown your com - pas - sion, strength, and love,
from bond - age to free - dom, you brought them forth,
brought them in - to a land that flows with life,
you show mer - cy on those of low de - gree,

for your love is nev - er - end - ing.

*Words:* Based on Psalm 136; versified by Marty Haugen
*Music:* Marty Haugen

# Psalm 91 205

Refrain

The Lord will raise you up on ea-gles' wings, bear you on the breath of dawn, make you to shine like the sun, and hold you in the palm of his hand.

Those who go to God Most High for safety
    will be protected by the Almighty.
I will say to the Lord, "You are my place of safety and protection.
    You are my God and I trust you." *Refrain*

God will save you from hidden traps
    and from deadly diseases.
He will cover you with his feathers,
    and under his wings you can hide.
His truth will be your shield and protection. *Refrain*

The Lord is your protection;
    you have made God Most High your place of safety.
Nothing bad will happen to you;
    no disaster will come to your home.
He has put his angels in charge of you
    to watch over you wherever you go. *Refrain*

*Words:* Michael Joncas, 1979
*Music:* Michael Joncas, 1979; harmonized by Norma de Waal Malefyt, 1992

ON EAGLES' WINGS

# 206 It Makes No Difference

1 It makes no dif - ference who we are, what
2 It makes no dif - ference where we live, in
3 It makes no dif - ference how we look, what
4 It makes a dif - ference how we treat our

lan - guage we may speak;
ci - ty, town, or farm;
col - or is our skin;
neigh - bors and our friends;

God loves us all and

*Refrain*

hears our prayers— he knows our needs and cares.

*Optional endings*

1-3 (cares.)

4

*Words:* Doris Clare Demaree; adapted by Bert Polman, 1993
*Music:* Sean E. Ivory, 1993
Words © 1994, CRC Publications. Music © 1994, Sean E. Ivory.

86 86
FULTON

# God Is So Good 207

1 God is so good, God is so good,

God is so good, he's so good to me.

2 He cares for me ....
3 God answers prayer ....
4 I praise his name ....

*Descant*

*Stanza 1 in different languages:*

*Korean:* Cho-u-shin Ha-na-nim, Cho-u-shin Ha-na-nim,
cham cho-u-shin, na ui Ha-na-nim.

*Spanish:* Dios es muy bue-no, Dios es muy bue-no,
Dios es muy bue-no, es muy bue-no pa-ra mi.

*Swahili:* Mungu yu M-we-ma, Mungu yu M-we-ma,
Mungu yu M-we-ma, Yu m-we-ma Kwan-gu.

*Words and Music:* traditional; descant by Susan Nipp

# 208 Psalm 27

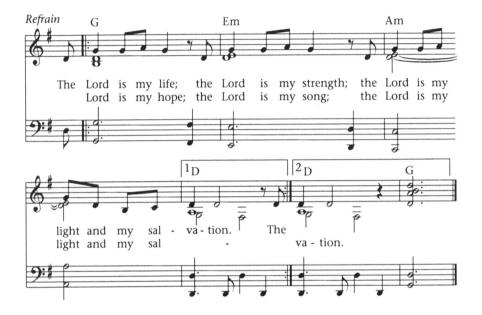

Refrain

The Lord is my life; the Lord is my strength; the Lord is my
Lord is my hope; the Lord is my song; the Lord is my

light and my sal - va - tion. The
light and my sal - va - tion.

The Lord is my light and my salvation;
  whom shall I fear?
The Lord is the stronghold of my life;
  of whom shall I be afraid? *Refrain*

One thing I asked of the Lord,
  that will I seek after:
to live in the house of the Lord
  all the days of my life,
to behold the beauty of the Lord,
  and to inquire in his temple.
For he will hide me in his shelter
  in the day of trouble;
he will conceal me under the cover of his tent;
  he will set me high on a rock. *Refrain*

Now my head is lifted up
  above my enemies all around me,
and I will offer in his tent
  sacrifices with shouts of joy;
I will sing and make melody to the Lord. *Refrain*

*Words:* from Psalm 27 (NIV); refrain by Michael Joncas, b. 1951
*Music:* Michael Joncas

# Amazing Grace 209

1 A - maz - ing grace— how sweet the sound— that
2 'Twas grace that taught my heart to fear, and
3 The Lord has prom - ised good to me, his

saved a wretch like me! I once was lost but
grace my fears re - lieved; how pre - cious did that
word my hope se - cures; he will my shield and

now am found, was blind but now I see.
grace ap - pear the hour I first be - lieved!
por - tion be as long as life en - dures.

4 Through many dangers, toils, and snares
    I have already come;
  'tis grace hath brought me safe thus far,
    and grace will lead me home.

5 When we've been there ten thousand years,
    bright shining as the sun,
  we've no less days to sing God's praise
    than when we'd first begun.

*Words:* stanzas 1-4, John Newton, 1779; stanza 5, *A Collection of Sacred Ballads*, 1790
*Music: Virginia Harmony*, 1831; arranged by Emily R. Brink, 1992
Arr. © 1994, CRC Publications

CM
NEW BRITAIN

# 210 If You But Trust in God to Guide You

1 If you but trust in God to guide you
2 On - ly be still and wait his plea - sure
3 Sing, pray, and keep his ways un - swerv - ing,

and place your con - fi - dence in him, you'll find him
in cheer - ful hope with heart con - tent. He fills your
of - fer your ser - vice faith - ful - ly, and trust his

al - ways there be - side you to give you hope and
needs to full - est mea - sure with what dis - cern - ing
word; though un - de - serv - ing, you'll find his prom - ise

strength with - in; for those who trust God's change - less
love has sent; doubt not our in - most wants are
true to be. God nev - er will for - sake in

*Words:* Georg Neumark, 1641
*Music:* Georg Neumark, 1657; arranged by Emily R. Brink, 1993
Arr. © 1994, CRC Publications

98 98 88
WER NUR DEN LIEBEN GOTT
Capo 3

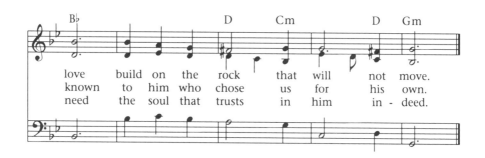

| | | | | | | | | | |
|---|---|---|---|---|---|---|---|---|---|
| love | build | on | the | rock | that | will | not | move. |
| known | to | him | who | chose | us | for | his | own. |
| need | the | soul | that | trusts | in | him | in - | deed. |

*Descant*

# 211 Everywhere I Go

1 Ev - ery-where I go, the Lord is near me.
2 In the dark of night should things a - larm me,
4 In the com - ing days of joy or sad - ness,
5 Ev - ery-where I go, the Lord is near me.

If I call up - on him, he will hear me.
ev - er in his sight, no ill may harm me.
I will praise his name with songs of glad - ness.
If I call up - on him, he will hear me.

Nev - er will I fear, for the Lord is near, ev - ery-where I
I will be of cheer, for the Lord is near, ev - ery-where I
For to me it's clear that the Lord is near, ev - ery-where I
Nev - er will I fear, for the Lord is near, ev - ery-where I

go.                    go.

*Words and Music:* Natalie Sleeth, 1975; arranged by Charlotte Larsen, 1992
Words and melody © 1975, Choristers Guild.

3 He is with me day by day; he will be my strength and stay;

from his path I will not stray but fol-low in his way.

*D.C. al Fine*

*Descant for instrument or voices on stanza 5*

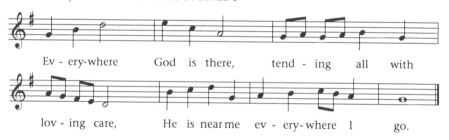

Ev - ery-where God is there, tend - ing all with

lov - ing care, He is near me ev - ery-where I go.

# 212 Trust in the Lord

Trust in the Lord with all your heart and lean not
on your own un - der - stand - ing. In all your ways ac-
know - ledge him, and he shall di - rect your paths.

*Words:* Proverbs 3:5-6 (NKJV)
*Music:* Frank Hernandez, 1990; arranged by Norma de Waal Malefyt, 1992

# Trust and Obey 213

When we walk with the Lord in the light of his
While we do his good will he a-bides with us

Word, what a glo-ry he sheds on our way!
still, and with all who will

trust and o-bey. Trust and o-bey, for there's

no oth-er way to be hap-py in

Je-sus but to trust and o-bey.

*Words:* John H. Sammis, 1887
*Music:* Daniel B. Towner, 1887

669 D with refrain
TRUST AND OBEY
Capo 3

# 214 I Want Jesus to Walk with Me

1 I want Jesus to walk with me;
2 In my trials, Lord, walk with me;
3 When I'm in trouble, Lord, walk with me;

I want Jesus to walk with me;
in my trials, Lord, walk with me;
when I'm in trouble, Lord, walk with me;

all along my pilgrim journey,
when my heart is almost breaking,
when my head is bowed in sorrow,

Lord, I want Jesus to walk with me.
Lord, I want Jesus to walk with me.
Lord, I want Jesus to walk with me.

*Words and Music:* African-American spiritual

WALK WITH ME

# Those Who Wait upon the Lord 215

1 Those who wait up-on the Lord shall re-new their strength,
2 Those who love the God of life shall re-new their strength,
3 Those who live a life of love shall re-new their strength,

they shall mount up on wings as ea-gles;

they shall run and not be wea-ry, they shall walk and not faint.

Help us, Lord; help us, Lord, in your way.

4 Those who offer gifts of praise . . . .
5 Those who grow in his wisdom . . . .
6 Those who seek first his kingdom . . . .
7 Those who wait upon the Lord . . . .

*Words and Music:* Stuart Hamblen, based on Isaiah 40:31; arranged by
Emily R. Brink, 1993
© 1953, Hamblen Music Co. Used by permission.

TEACH ME LORD
Capo 2

# 216 Psalm 46

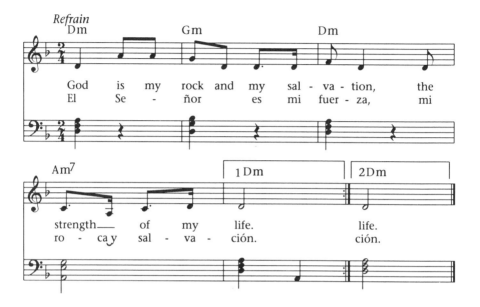

*Refrain*

God is my rock and my sal - va - tion, the
El Se - ñor es mi fuer - za, mi

strength___ of my life. life.
ro - ca y sal - va - ción. ción.

God is our refuge and strength,
    an ever-present help in trouble.
Therefore we will not fear, though the earth give way
    and the mountains fall into the heart of the sea,
though its waters roar and foam
    and the mountains quake with their surging. *Refrain*

There is a river whose streams make glad the city of God,
    the holy place where the Most High dwells.
God is within her, she will not fall;
    God will help her at break of day.
Nations are in uproar, kingdoms fall;
    he lifts his voice, the earth melts. *Refrain*

Come and see the works of the Lord,
    the desolations he has brought on the earth.
He makes wars cease to the ends of the earth;
    he breaks the bow and shatters the spear,
    he burns the shields with fire.
"Be still and know that I am God;
    I will be exalted among the nations,
    I will be exalted in the earth." *Refrain*

*Words:* Psalm 46 (NIV)
*Music:* Refrain by Juan A. Espinosa, 1978

Capo 5

# Protect Me, God: I Trust in You 217

1 Pro - tect me, God: I trust in you. I tell you now,
2 Your peo - ple are a cho - sen race, and I de - light
3 Lord God, you are my food and drink; my work for you
4 Thank you, my Lord, for warn-ing me; by night and day

"You are my Lord; on you my hap - pi - ness de - pends."
in faith - ful friends, but pa - gan ways I will not share.
is joy in - deed; glad is the her - i - tage that's mine.
you guide my thoughts. With you be - fore me, I stand firm.

Pro - tect me, God: I trust in you.

Descant

Flute or Violin

Cello or Piano

*Words:* Psalm 16; versified by Michael Saward, 1970
*Music:* M. Christian T. Strover, 1973; arranged by Charlotte Larson, 1992;
    descant by Emily R. Brink, 1991

888 with refrain
MEPHIBOSHETH
Capo 3

# 218 When I Am Afraid

*Words:* Frank Hernandez; based on Psalm 56:3-4a
*Music:* Frank Hernandez; arranged by Emily R. Brink, 1994

fraid, in God I trust, in God, whose word I praise. in

## Our Help 219

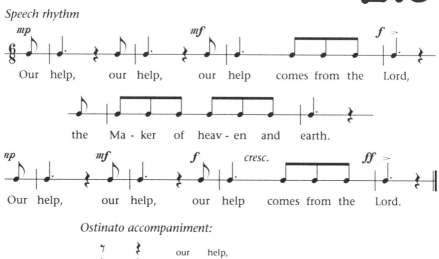

*Speech rhythm*

Our help, our help, our help comes from the Lord,

the Ma - ker of heav - en and earth.

Our help, our help, our help comes from the Lord.

*Ostinato accompaniment:*

our help,

Our help,

*Words:* Psalm 121:2; Psalm 124:8
*Music:* Richard L. Van Oss, 1992
© 1994, CRC Publications

# 220 Lead Me, Guide Me

*Words and Music:* Doris M. Akers; arranged by Richard Smallwood, 1981

LEAD ME
Capo 1

# 221 Day By Day

Day by day, dear Lord, for these three things I pray: to see you more clear-ly, to love you more dear-ly, to fol-low you more near-ly day by day.

*Words:* Richard of Chichester, 1197-1253
*Music:* D. Austin; harmonized by Richard L. Van Oss, 1992
© D. Austin

Capo 5

# I Belong to God 222

*(hands on chest)*
You made ev-ery part of me, and I be-long to you. I'll

*(point to mouth)*
lift my voice to sing for you,

*(hands outstretched)*
lift my hands to work for you,

*(point to eyes)*
use my eyes to see your world,

*(point to ears)*
use my ears to hear your word.

*(hands on chest)*
You made ev-ery part of me, and I be-long to you.

*Words and Music:* Marie Pooler, altered by Helen Kemp

Capo 5

# 223 **Believe in the Lord**

*Words:* Acts 16:31
*Music:* Frank Hernandez

saved.  Be - lieve  in  the  Lord  Je - sus  Christ.

## Be Still 224

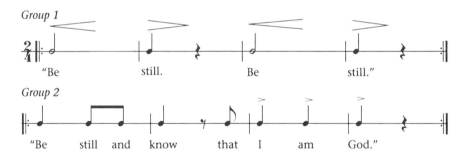

*Group 1*

"Be        still.        Be        still."

*Group 2*

"Be    still   and    know    that    I    am    God."

*After one person begins by announcing "And God said,"*
*group 1 begins with a hushed articulate command; group 2 adds their*
*voices; then group 1 continues alone, diminishing toward the end.*

*Words:* Psalm 46:10
*Music:* Betty Ann Ramseth, 1970
Reprinted from *That I May Speak*, © 1970, Augsburg Publishing House. Reprinted by permission of Augsburg Fortress.

# 225 Be Still and Know

1 Be still and know that I am God.
2 I am the Lord who heals your life.
3 In you, O Lord, we put our trust.

Be still and know that I am God.
I am the Lord who heals your life.
In you, O Lord, we put our trust.

Be still and know that I am God.
I am the Lord who heals your life.
In you, O Lord, we put our trust.

*Words:* anonymous, based on Psalm 46:10; 7:1; Exodus 15:26
*Music:* anonymous; arranged by Norma de Waal Malefyt, 1992
Arr. © 1994, CRC Publications

888
BE STILL AND KNOW

# I Have Decided to Follow Jesus 226

1 I have de - cid - ed to fol - low Je - sus, I have de - cid - ed to fol - low Je - sus, I have de - cid - ed to fol - low Je - sus— no turn - ing back, no turn - ing back.

2 The world behind me, the cross before me—(3x)
  no turning back, no turning back.

3 Though none go with me, I still will follow . . . .

4 Will you decide now to follow Jesus? . . .

*Words and Music:* anonymous

# 227 Standing On the Lord's Side

"Tell me, whose side are you stand-ing on?" "I'm stand-ing on the Lord's side." "Whose side are you stand-ing on?" "Stand-ing on the Lord's side. I stand, I stand, I stand, I stand— stand-ing on the Lord's side. I stand, I stand, I stand, I stand— stand-ing on the Lord's side."

*Words and Music:* traditional; arranged by Emily R. Brink, 1992
Arr. © 1994, CRC Publications

# Psalm 139 228

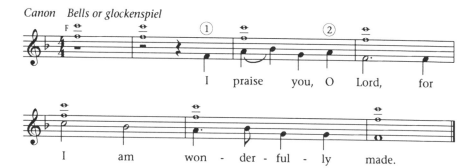

Lord, you have examined me
and know all about me.
You know when I sit down and when I get up.
You know my thoughts before I think them.
You know where I go and where I lie down.
You know thoroughly everything I do.
Lord, even before I say a word, you already know it. *Refrain*

You made my whole being;
you formed me in my mother's body.
I praise you because you made me in an
amazing and wonderful way.
What you have done is wonderful.
I know this very well. *Refrain*

You saw my bones being formed
as I took shape in my mother's body.
When I was put together there,
you saw my body as it was formed.
All the days planned for me
were written in your book
before I was one day old. *Refrain*

God, your thoughts are precious to me.
They are so many!
If I could count them,
they would be more than all the grains of sand. *Refrain*

*Words:* Psalm 139:1-4, 13-18 (NIV); refrain by Randolph Currie
*Music:* Randolph Currie

# 229 Psalm 1

*Canon*

Hap-py are they who hope, who hope in the Lord.

Happy are those
  who do not follow the advice of the wicked,
or take the path that sinners tread,
  or sit in the seat of scoffers;
but their delight is in the law of the Lord
  and on his law they meditate day and night.  *Refrain*

They are like trees
  planted by the streams of water,
which yield their fruit in its season,
  and their leaves do not wither.
In all that they do, they prosper.  *Refrain*

The wicked are not so,
  but are like chaff that the wind drives away.
Therefore the wicked will not stand in the judgement,
  nor sinners in the congregation of the righteous;
for the Lord watches over the way of the righteous,
  but the way of the wicked will perish.  *Refrain*

*Orff instrument patterns*
  *Alto metallophone*   *Soprano xylophone*

*Words:* Psalm 1 (NRSV); refrain by Robert J. Thompson
*Music:* Robert J. Thompson; arranged by Emily R. Brink, 1994

# Rejoice in the Lord Always 230

**Round**

1. Re - joice in the Lord al - ways, and a - gain I say, Re - joice! *(clap)*

2. Re - joice in the Lord al - ways, and a - gain I say, Re - joice!

3. Re - joice! Re - joice! And a - gain I say, Re - joice!

4. Re - joice! Re - joice! And a - gain I say, Re - joice!

**Orff instruments**

*Alto metallophone*  *Glockenspiel*

*Words:* Philippians 4:4
*Music:* traditional; arranged by Emily R. Brink, 1993
Arr. © 1994, CRC Publications

REJOICE
Capo 3

# 231 Jesus, Jesus, Let Us Tell You

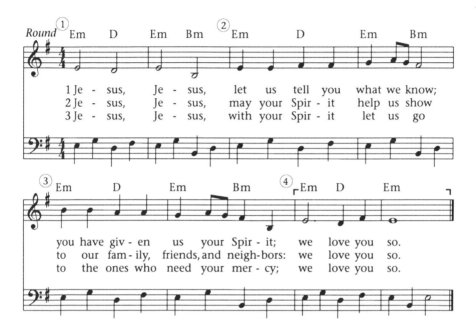

1 Je - sus, Je - sus, let us tell you what we know;
2 Je - sus, Je - sus, may your Spir - it help us show
3 Je - sus, Je - sus, with your Spir - it let us go

you have giv - en us your Spir - it; we love you so.
to our fam - ily, friends, and neigh-bors: we love you so.
to the ones who need your mer - cy; we love you so.

**Orff instruments**

*Bass xylophone*    *Alto glockenspiel*

*Soprano glockenspiel*    *Alto or soprano xylophone*

*Another traditional stanza, "The Love Round":*

4 Love, love, love, love,
Christians this is your call:
Love our neighbors as ourselves
for God loves us all.

*Words:* Stanzas 1 and 4, traditional; stanza 2, Bert Polman; stanza 3, Joanne Hamilton
*Music:* traditional; arranged by Richard L. Van Oss, 1992
© 1994, CRC Publications

# Christ, You Are the Fullness 232

1 Christ, you are the full-ness of God, first - born of
2 Since we have been raised with you, Lord, help keep our
3 Help us live in peace as true mem-bers of your

ev-ery-thing. For by you___ all things were___
hearts and minds pure and set on things that build your
bod - y. Let your word dwell rich - ly in us

made; you hold them up. You are head of the
rule o'er all the earth. All our life is now
as we teach and sing. Thanks and praise be to

church, which is your bod - y. First - born from the
hid - den with___ you in God. When you come a -
God through you, Lord Je - sus. In what-e'er we

dead, you in all things are su - preme!
gain, we will share your glo - ry.
do let your name re - ceive the praise!

*Descant*

*play 4 times*

*Orff instrument patterns*
*Bass xylophone*   *Alto metallophone*   *Glockenspiel or bells*

*Play pitches softly in ran-
dom order, not in a row.*

*Words:* Colossians 1:15-18; 3:1-4, 15-17; versified by Bert Polman, 1986
*Music:* Korean; arranged by Emily R. Brink, 1994
Text © 1987, arr. © 1994, CRC Publications

# 233 Discipleship

Refrain

What does it mean to fol-low Je-sus? What does it mean to go his way? What does it mean to do what he wants me to, ev - ery day? ev - ery day?

1 I can love my neigh-bor, just as Je - sus
2 I can say I'm sor - ry when I've done some

*Words and Music:* Lois Brokering
© 1990, Herb Associates. Used by permission.

Capo 3

# 234 Time to Pray

1 Time to pray, time to say, thank you, God, thank you, God,
2 Time to sing, time to bring, praise to God, praise to God,
3 Time to live, time to give all to God, all to God.

for our loved ones far and near, for our friends and
in the night and in the day, ev - ery-thing we
When the need - y seek our door, give un - til we

neigh-bors here. Thank you, God. Thank you, God.
do and say. Praise to God. Praise to God.
have no more. All is God's. All is God's.

*Words and Music:* Joe Pinson, 1975

Capo 1

# For the Fruit of All Creation 235

F    Bb    G    C    Bb  C7    F

1 For  the fruit  of    all    cre - a - tion, thanks  be  to God.
2 In    the  just  re - ward  of la - bor,  God's  will  be done.
3 For  the har - vests  of    the Spir - it,  thanks  be  to God.

Bb    G    C    Bb  C7    F

For  his gifts  to    ev - ery na - tion,  thanks  be  to  God.
In  the  help  we  give  our neigh - bor,  God's  will  be  done.
For  the good  we    all  in - her - it,  thanks  be  to  God.

Bb        F        Dm    Gm

For  the plow - ing,  sow - ing, reap - ing,  si - lent growth while  we  are
In  our world - wide  task of car - ing  for  the  hun - gry  and de -
For  the won - ders  that as - tound us,  for  the truths that  still con -

C    F    Bb    G    C    Bb  C7    F

sleep - ing, fu - ture needs in  earth's safe - keep - ing, thanks  be  to God.
spair - ing,  in  the har - vests  we  are shar - ing,  God's will  be done.
found us,  most of  all,  that  love  has found us,  thanks  be  to God.

*Words:* Fred Pratt Green, 1970
*Music:* Traditional Welsh melody, c. 1784; harmonized by Luther O. Emerson, 1906

84 84 88 84
AR HYD Y NOS
Capo 5

# 236 We Are the Church

*Refrain*

I am the church! You are the church!

We are the church to-geth-er! All who fol-low Je-sus,

all a-round the world, yes, we're the church to-geth-er!

1 The church is not a build-ing, the
2 We're man-y kinds of peo-ple with
3 And when the peo-ple gath-er, there's
4 At Pen-te-cost some peo-ple re-

*Words and Music:* Richard Avery and Donald Marsh

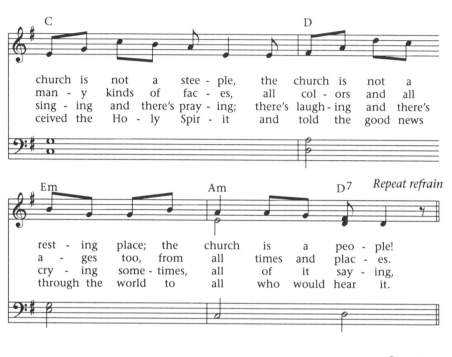

church is not a stee - ple, the church is not a
man - y kinds of fac - es, all col - ors and all
sing - ing and there's pray - ing; there's laugh - ing and there's
ceived the Ho - ly Spir - it and told the good news

rest - ing place; the church is a peo - ple!
a - ges too, from all times and plac - es.
cry - ing some - times, all of it say - ing,
through the world to all who would hear it.

*Repeat refrain*

## Let Us Love  237

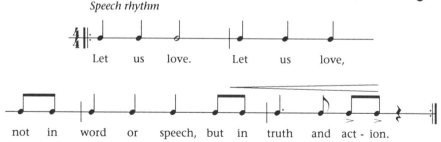

*Speech rhythm*

Let us love. Let us love,

not in word or speech, but in truth and act - ion.

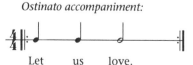

*Ostinato accompaniment:*

Let us love.

*Words:* 1 John 3:18, NRSV
*Music:* Emily R. Brink, 1992
© 1994, CRC Publications

# 238 Children of the Lord

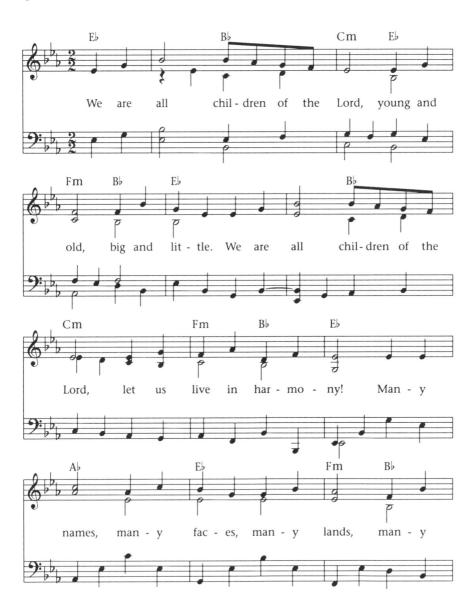

We are all chil-dren of the Lord, young and
old, big and lit - tle. We are all chil-dren of the
Lord, let us live in har - mo - ny! Man - y
names, man - y fac - es, man - y lands, man - y

*Words and Music:* Natalie Sleeth, adapted from the anthem "Children of the Lord"
© 1976, Hinshaw Music, Inc. Used by permission.

Capo 3

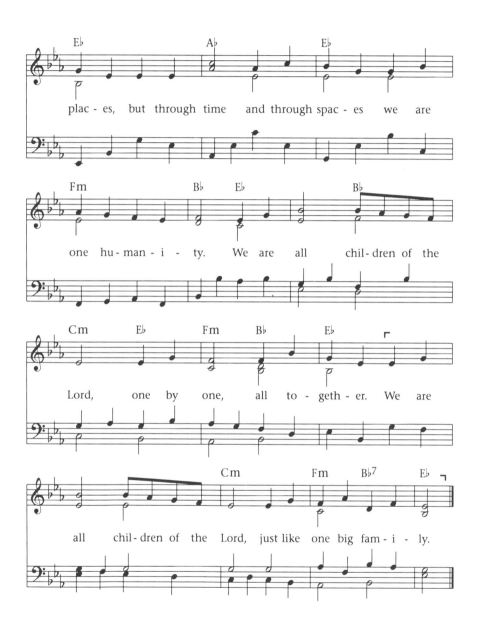

# 239 Shine, Jesus, Shine

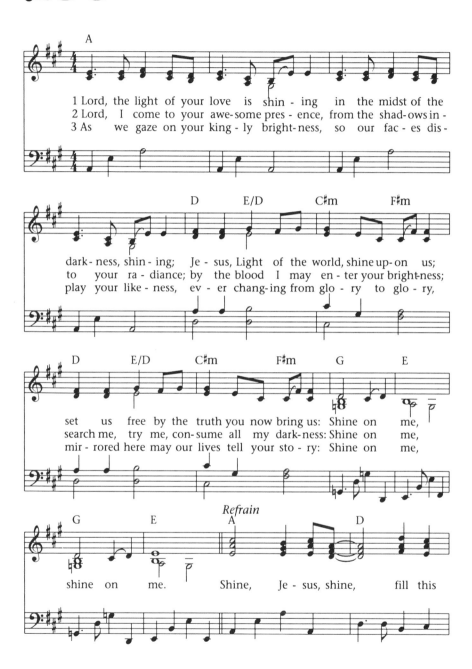

1 Lord, the light of your love is shin-ing in the midst of the
2 Lord, I come to your awe-some pres-ence, from the shad-ows in-
3 As we gaze on your king-ly bright-ness, so our fac-es dis-

dark-ness, shin-ing; Je-sus, Light of the world, shine up-on us;
to your ra-diance; by the blood I may en-ter your bright-ness;
play your like-ness, ev-er chang-ing from glo-ry to glo-ry,

set us free by the truth you now bring us: Shine on me,
search me, try me, con-sume all my dark-ness: Shine on me,
mir-rored here may our lives tell your sto-ry: Shine on me,

*Refrain*

shine on me. Shine, Je-sus, shine, fill this

*Words and Music:* Graham Kendrick, 1987

SHINE, JESUS, SHINE
Capo 2

land with the Fa - ther's glo - ry. Blaze, Spir - it, blaze, set our

hearts on fire. Flow, riv - er, flow, flood the

na - tions with grace and mer - cy. Send forth your Word, Lord, and

let there be light!

# 240 There's No God as Great
# No Hay Dios tan Grande

There's no god as great as you, O Lord, O___
No hay dios tan gran-de co - mo tú, no lo

Lord, my___ God. There's no god who works the might-y
hay, no lo hay. No hay dios que pue - da ha - cer las

won - ders, all the won - ders that you do.
o - bras co - mo las que ha - ces tú.

do. Not by our weap-ons, nor by our pow - er, but by your
tú. No es con es - pa - da, ni con e - jér-ci-to, mas con tu

*Words and Music:* Spanish; translated for *Psalter Hymnal,* 1987

NO HAY DIOS
Capo 1

# 241 Go into the World

Descant

3 Go ye now and

1 Go ye, go ye in - to the world, and
2 Go ye, go ye in - to the world, and
3 Go ye, go ye in - to the world, and

tell the sto - ry to all be - liev - ers. Go ye

make dis - ci - ples of all the na - tions.
take the gos - pel to all the peo - ple. Go ye, go ye
tell the sto - ry to all be - liev - ers.

now, and I will be with you there!

in - to the world, and I will be with you there!

*Words and Music:* Natalie Sleeth, based on Matthew 28:19-20; adapted from the anthem "Go into the World"

## If You Believe and I Believe 242

If you be-lieve and I be-lieve and we to-geth-er pray,

the Ho - ly Spir - it will come down and set God's peo - ple free,

and set God's peo - ple free,       and set God's peo - ple free;

the Ho - ly Spir - it will come down and set God's peo - ple free.

*Words:* from Zimbabwe, based on Matthew 18:19
*Music:* from Zimbabwe, as adapted from an English song

# 243 Here I Am, Lord

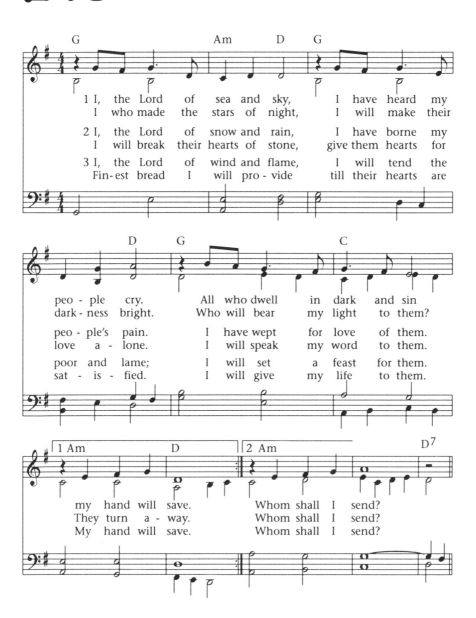

1 I, the Lord of sea and sky, I have heard my
I who made the stars of night, I will make their

2 I, the Lord of snow and rain, I have borne my
I will break their hearts of stone, give them hearts for

3 I, the Lord of wind and flame, I will tend the
Fin-est bread I will pro-vide till their hearts are

peo-ple cry. All who dwell in dark and sin
dark-ness bright. Who will bear my light to them?

peo-ple's pain. I have wept for love of them.
love a-lone. I will speak my word to them.

poor and lame; I will set a feast for them.
sat-is-fied. I will give my life to them.

my hand will save. Whom shall I send?
They turn a-way. Whom shall I send?
My hand will save. Whom shall I send?

*Words:* Daniel L. Schutte, 1981; based on Isaiah 6:8
*Music:* Daniel L. Schutte, 1981; adapted by Carlton R. Young, 1988

77 74 D with refrain
HERE I AM, LORD

# 244 Let Me Be Your Servant, Jesus

1 Let me be your hands, Lord Je - sus, help - ing those who
2 Let me be your voice, Lord Je - sus, tell - ing peo - ple
3 Let me be your ears, Lord Je - sus, hear - ing those who

come my way. Let me be your feet, Lord Je - sus,
of your love. Let me share your work, Lord Je - sus,
cry for help. Let me share in help - ing oth - ers

run - ning er - rands ev - ery day.
me on earth and you a - bove. *Refrain* Hands and feet, a
and not just think of my - self.

voice to bring good news, great news of our King. Let me

be your ser - vant, Je - sus, help - ing you in ev - ery way.

*Words and Music:* Judith A. Helms, 1980

# When Did We See You 245

1 "Come now, you bless - ed, eat at my ta - ble,"
2 When did we see you hun - gry or thirs - ty?
3 "When you gave bread to the earth's hun - gry chil - dren,
4 Christ, when we see you out on life's road - ways,

said Je - sus Christ to the right - eous a - bove.
When were you home - less, a strang - er a - lone?
when you gave shel - ter to war's ref - u - gees.
look - ing to us in the fac - es of need,

"When I was hun - gry, thirs - ty, and home - less,
When did we see you sick or in pris - on?
When you re - mem - bered those most for - got - ten,
then may we know you, wel - come and show you

sick and in pris - on, you showed me your love."
What have we done that you call us your own?
you cared for me in the small - est of these."
love that is faith - ful in word and in deed.

*Words:* Ruth Duck, 1979
*Music:* Emily R. Brink, 1992

Capo 1

# 246 You and I

1 Who's goin' to tell the sto - ry? You and I!
2 Who's goin' to bring the king - dom? You and I!
4 Who's goin' to feed the hun - gry? You and I!

Tell of the Lord's great glo - ry? You and I!
Who's goin' to spread the gos - pel? You and I!
Care for the sick and lone - ly? You and I!

Who's goin' to let the whole world know? Help his dis - ci - ples
Who's goin' to do the kind - ly deed? Com - fort the one in
Who's goin' to let the whole world see peo - ple can live in

grow and mul - ti - ply?
need and help sup - ply? You and I!
har - mo - ny? Let's try!

*Words and Music:* Natalie Sleeth, adapted from the anthem "You and I"
© 1976, Hinshaw Music, Inc. Used by permission.

Capo 1

# 247 When I Needed a Neighbor

2  I was hungry and thirsty, were you there? . . .

3  I was cold, I was naked, were you there? . . .

4  When I needed a shelter, were you there? . . .

5  Wherever you travel, I'll be there, I'll be there;
   wherever you travel, I'll be there.
   And the creed and the color and the name won't matter;
   I'll be there.

*Words and Music:* Sydney Carter, 1965

# The Servant Song 248

1 Will you let me be your ser-vant, let me be as
2 We are pil-grims on a jour-ney; we are travel-ers
3 I will hold the Christ-light for you in the night-time

Christ to you? Pray that I might have the grace to
on the road. We are here to help each oth-er
of your fear. I will hold my hand out to you,

let you be my ser - vant too.
walk the mile and bear the load.
speak the peace you long to hear.

4 I will weep when you are weeping;
when you laugh, I'll laugh with you.
I will share your joy and sorrow
till we've seen this journey through.

5 Will you let me be your servant,
let me be as Christ to you?
Pray that I might have the grace to
let you be my servant too.

*Words and Music:* Richard Gillard; arranged by Emily R. Brink, 1992

# 249 Sent by the Lord

Sent by the Lord am I; my hands are rea-dy now to make the earth the place in which the king-dom comes. The an-gels can-not change a world of hurt and pain in-to a world of love, of jus-tice and of peace. The task is mine to do, to set it real-ly free. Oh,

*Words:* Cuban oral tradition; translated by Jorge Maldonado, 1991
*Music:* traditional Cuban; arranged by Iona Community, 1991

Capo 1

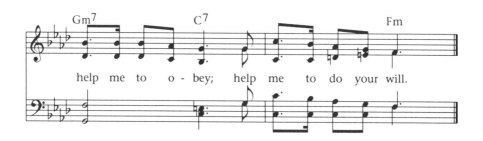

help me to o - bey; help me to do your will.

## On the Poor 250

1 On the poor, on the poor, show your mer - cy, O Lord.

On the poor, on the poor, show your mer - cy, O Lord.

2 On the poor, on the poor, show your mercy, O Christ. . . .
3 On the poor, on the poor, show your mercy, O Lord. . . .

*Words:* adapted traditional liturgical text
*Music:* from Paraguay
Arr. © 1991, Iona Community. Used by permission of G.I.A. Publications.

66 66
KYRIE GUARANY

# 251 Jesu, Jesu, Fill Us with Your Love

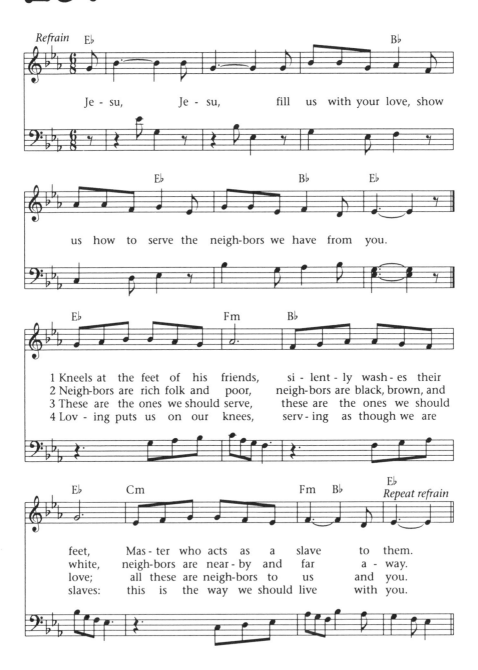

*Refrain*

Je - su, Je - su, fill us with your love, show

us how to serve the neigh-bors we have from you.

1 Kneels at the feet of his friends, si - lent - ly wash - es their
2 Neigh-bors are rich folk and poor, neigh-bors are black, brown, and
3 These are the ones we should serve, these are the ones we should
4 Lov - ing puts us on our knees, serv - ing as though we are

*Repeat refrain*

feet, Mas - ter who acts as a slave to them.
white, neigh-bors are near - by and far a - way.
love; all these are neigh-bors to us and you.
slaves: this is the way we should live with you.

*Words and Music:* folk song from Ghana, adapted by Tom Colvin; music arranged by Robert Roth

779 with refrain
CHEREPONI
Capo 1

# Send Me, Lord 252

THUMA MINA
Capo 5

# Copyright Holders

Each song under copyright, whether text, tune, or arrangement, is so indicated at the bottom of each song page. If you wish to reproduce (or reprint) any copyrighted words or music contained in this book, please contact the copyright holder for permission.

Abingdon Press
201 8th Ave. So.
Nashville, TN 37202
(615) 749–6422

Augsburg Fortress Publishers
426 S Fifth St
Box 1209
Minneapolis MN 55440
(612) 330–3300

D. Austin
Rose Hill School
Alderly
Wooton–Under–Edge, Glos
England

A. C. Barham–Gould Estate
c/o D. R. Gould
34 Pollards Dr.
Horsham, West Sussex RH 13 5HH
England

Benson Music Group, Inc.
365 Great Circle Rd.
Nashville, TN 37228
(615) 742–6924

Loje Braen
560 Bellview
Winchester, VA 22601

Broadman Press
127 Ninth Avenue North
Nashville, TN 37234
(615) 251–2533

Brummhart Publishing Co.
12 Twinshaven Rd.
Napanoch, NY 12458

AnnaMae Meyer Bush
850 Byerly SE
Grand Rapids, MI 49546
(616) 949–2454

Carl Fischer, Inc.
62 Cooper Sq.
New York, NY 10003
(212) 777–0900

Dosia Carlson
Beatitudes Center D.O.A.R.
555 W. Glendale Ave.
Phoenix, AZ 85021

Gerhard M. Cartford
2279 Commonwealth Ave.
St. Paul, MN 55108

Rev. Brian C. Casebow
25 Fountainhall Rd.
Edinburgh EH9 2LN
Scotland

Choristers Guild
2834 W. Kingsley Road
Garland, TX 75041
(214) 271–1521

Christian Conference of Asia
Attn: Rev. Toshitsugu Arai
Pak Tin Village, Mei Tin Road
Shatin, N.T.
Hong Kong

Concordia Publishing
3558 Jefferson Ave.
St. Louis, MO 62118
(314)664–7000

The Copyright Company
Maranatha! Music
40 Music Sq. East
Nashville, TN 37203
(615) 244–5588

Covenant Press
5101 N. Francisco Ave.
Chicago, IL 60625
(312) 784–3000

E.C.S. Publishing
138 Ipswich
Boston, MA 02215
(617) 236–1935

Editoria Sinodal
rua Epifanio Fogaca 467
Caixa Postal 11
93001 Sao Leopoldo, R.S.
BRAZIL

Stanley M. Farr
518 Fairmont Rd.
Morgantown, WV 26505

Frederick Harris Music Company
340 Nagel Drive
Buffalo, NY 14225
(800) 387–4013

Dorothy Frisch
6160 Rice Creek Dr.
Fridley, MN 55432

G. I. A. Publications
7404 S. Mason Ave.
Chicago, IL 60638
(708)496–3800

Hamblen Music Company
26101 Ravenhill Rd.
Canyon Country, CA 91350
(805) 252–3881

Mr. Nobuaki Hanaoka
Japanese United Methodist Church
6929 Franklin Blvd.
Sacramento, CA 95823

Harper Collins Religious
77–85 Fulham Palace Rd.
Hammersmith
London W68JB, England

Judith Helms
21 Beverly Drive
Arcata CA 95521

Herb Associates
11641 Palmer Rd.
Bloomington, MN 55437–3437
(612) 888–5281

Hinshaw Music
P. O. Box 470
Chapel Hill, NC 27514
(919) 933–1691

Hope Publishing Company
380 S. Main Pl.
Carol Stream, IL 60188
(800) 323–1049

Stephan Hopkinson
Duke's Watch
2 S. Swithen St.
Winchester, SO23 9JP
England

Integrated Copyright Group
Lillenas Publishing Co.
P. O. Box 24149
Nashville, TN 37202
(615) 329–3999

Integrity Music, Inc.
1000 Cody Road
Mobile, AL 36695
(205) 633–9000

Sean Ivory
1138 Hall St SE
Grand Rapids MI 49507

Kevin Mayhew Publishers
Rattlesden
Bury St. Edmunds
Suffolk 1P30 0SZ
England

Manna Music, Inc.
P. O. Box 218
Pacific City, OR 97135
(503) 965–6112

Rev. John A. Moss
101 Amherst Rd.
South Hadley, MA 01075

Music Anno Domini
P. O. Box 7465
Grand Rapids, MI 49510
(616) 241–3787

New Dawn Music
P. O. Box 13248
Portland, OR 97213
(800) 243–3296

OCP Publications
5536 NE Hassalo
Portland OR 97213
(800) 243–3296

Oxford University Press
Music Dept.
Walton Street
Oxford OX2 6DP
England
Fax 0865–56646

Paulist Press
997 Macarthur Blvd.
Mahway, NJ 07430
(201) 825–7300

Joe Pinson
HCSR
Box 491
Denton, TX 76202

Prism Tree Music
Bob Kilpatrick Ministries
P. O . Box 2383
Fair Oaks, CA 95628
(916) 961–1022

Cary Ratcliff
226 Winstead St.
Rochester, NY 14609

David Ritsema
3955 South Oneida Street
Denver, CO 80237

Robert Roth
330 Morgan St.
Oberlin, OH 44074

Sacred Music Press
The Lorenz Corp.
501 E. 3rd Street
P. O. Box 802
Dayton, OH 45401
(800) 444–1144

G. Schirmer Music
c/o Music Sales Corp.
257 Park Ave. So.
New York, NY 10010

Silliman University
Ms. Elena Maquiso
Ulahingan Research Project
Dumaguete City, 6200
Phillippines

The Sparrow Corp.
P. O. Box 5010
101 Winners Circle
Brentwood, TN 37024
(615) 371–6800

Stainer & Bell, Ltd.
P. O. Box 110, Victoria House
23 Greneisen Road
Finchley, London N3 1DZ
England

Linda Stassen–Benjamin
New Songs Ministries
RR 1, Box 454
Erin TN 37061

Wim ter Burg
c/o G. F. Callenbach B.V.
Postbus 1086
Nijkerk 3860BB
The Netherlands

Unichappel Music, Inc.
Div. of Hal Leonard Publishing
7777 W. Bluemound Rd.
Milwaukee, WI 53213
(414) 774–3630

United Church Press
700 Prospect Ave. E.
Cleveland, OH 44115
(216) 736–3700

United Methodist Publishing House
201 – 8th Avenue So
Nashville TN 37202
(615) 749–6422

Coby Veenstra
Cricket Music Ministry
P. O. Box 133
Hampton, ON L0B 1J0
CANADA

Walton Music Corp.
170 NE 33rd Street
Ft. Lauderdale, FL 33334

Westminster John Knox Press
100 Witherspoon Street
Louisville, KY 40202
(800) 523–1631

Bert Witvoet
Calvinist Contact
261 Martindale Rd., Unit 4
St. Catharines, ON L2W 1A1
CANADA
(416) 682–8311

WORD Music
3319 West End Ave. Suite 200
Nashville, TN 37203
(615) 385–9673

World Library Publications
3815 N. Willow Rd.
Schiller Park. IL 60176
(708) 678–0621

John Ylvisaker
New Generation Publishing
Box 321
Waverly, IA 50677

# Capo Chart

Pianists may find "flat" keys easier to play than "sharp" keys. But the opposite is true for guitarists. Using a capo to clamp the strings allows a guitarist to transpose to a more convenient key. Shortening the strings by one fret (Capo 1) will raise the pitch a half step; clamping on the third fret (Capo 3) will raise the pitch three half steps.

The chart below shows how a capo can be used to play in more convenient keys. For example, by using Capo 3, a song in the key of F (with one flat) can be played as if in the key of D. The resulting sound from the shortened strings will actually be in F. All major and minor chords are listed.

Capo suggestions are made on the bottom right of many song pages. For those songs, find the key signature and key below, add the capo, and play the chords in parentheses. The resulting sound will be in the original key.

|  | Scale degree | | | | | | |
| --- | --- | --- | --- | --- | --- | --- | --- |
| Number of flats | 1 | 2 | 3 | 4 | 5 | 6 | 7 |
| Key of F capo 3 | F (D) | Gm (Em) | Am (F#m) | B♭ (G) | C (A) | Dm (Bm) | |
| Key of F capo 5 | F (C) | Gm (Dm) | Am (Em) | B♭ (F) | C (G) | Dm (Am) | |
| Key of Dm capo 5 | Dm (Am) | | F (C) | Gm (Dm) | A (E) | B♭ (F) | C (G) |
| Key of B♭ capo 1 | B♭ (A) | Cm (Bm) | Dm (C#m) | E♭ (D) | F (E) | Gm (F#m) | |
| Key of E♭ capo 1 | E♭ (D) | Fm (Em) | Gm (F#m) | A♭ (G) | B♭ (A) | Cm (Bm) | |
| Key of E♭ capo 3 | E♭ (C) | Fm (Dm) | Gm (Em) | A♭ (F) | B♭ (G) | Cm (Am) | |
| Key of Cm capo 5 | Cm (Gm) | | E♭ (B♭) | Fm (Cm) | G (D) | A♭ (E♭) | B♭ (F) |
| Key of A♭ capo 1 | Ab (G) | Bbm (Am) | Cm (Bm) | D♭ (C) | E♭ (D) | Fm (Em) | |
| Key of Fm capo 1 | Fm (Em) | | A♭ (G) | B♭m (Am) | C (B) | D♭b (C) | E♭ (D) |

# Index of First Lines and Titles